C. A. Jones

Stories for the Christian Year

Vol. 5

C. A. Jones

Stories for the Christian Year

Vol. 5

Reprint of the original, first published in 1875.

1st Edition 2024 | ISBN: 978-3-38525-199-1

Verlag (Publisher): Outlook Verlag GmbH, Zeilweg 44, 60439 Frankfurt, Deutschland
Vertretungsberechtigt (Authorized to represent): E. Roepke, Zeilweg 44, 60439 Frankfurt, Deutschland
Druck (Print): Books on Demand GmbH, In de Tarpen 42, 22848 Norderstedt, Deutschland

STORIES

FOR

THE CHRISTIAN YEAR.

BY

C. A. JONES,

AUTHOR OF "CHURCH STORIES," ETC

VOL. V.

Fifth Sunday after Trinity to the Fifteenth Sunday
after Trinity.

LONDON:

JOSEPH MASTERS AND CO., 78, NEW BOND STREET.

MDCCCLXXV.

CONTENTS.

Fifth Sunday after Trinity :   PAGE

   HARD WORDS 1

Sixth Sunday after Trinity :

   THROUGH THE SHADOWS . . . 25

Seventh Sunday after Trinity :

   APPLE POLLY 49

Eighth Sunday after Trinity :

   HURTFUL THINGS 73

Ninth Sunday after Trinity :

   HONEST BEN 97

Tenth Sunday after Trinity :

   A HERO AND A HEROINE . . . 121

Eleventh Sunday after Trinity :

   HARRY'S WREATH 145

Twelfth Sunday after Trinity :

   LITTLE WAX-WORKS 169

PAGE

Thirteenth Sunday after Trinity:

    GO AND DO THOU LIKEWISE . . . 193

Fourteenth Sunday after Trinity:

    BILL'S SISTER 217

Fifteenth Sunday after Trinity:

    THE LESSON THAT THE LILIES TAUGHT . 241

HARD WORDS.

Fifth Sunday after Trinity.

"Not rendering railing for railing, but contrariwise blessing."

"IT ain't much use to go home, for it's only to hear grumbling and complaining, and to be told it was a bad day when we two was married in the old Church. I suppose it was, and yet GOD knows I loved Jinny truly then, and I love her now, although nothing will make her believe it. I don't know where the fault has been, but I sometimes think that if we had done as the good old Parson told us to do, and kept to Church-going, and all the good ways we had been taught at home, that trouble might have come to us different like. I don't suppose it would have kept away, but we might have learnt to bear it better; anyhow, things can't be worse than they are, and I may as well smoke my pipe in comfort at the Hen and Chickens, as go home to be nagged at."

And the speaker, Ralph Hutton by name, a fine, stalwart young fellow, looked with a somewhat regretful expression towards the entrance of the narrow lane which led to his home. He hesitated for an instant, and something that looked very like a tear rolled down his sun-burnt cheek; then the momentary softness vanished, and was succeeded by a hard, somewhat dogged expression, and Ralph's Guardian Angel turned away in sorrow, for the young man had disregarded the warning voice of conscience—had forgotten all the old teaching of his boyhood—all the vows and promises he had made when he had knelt at the Altar of GOD, and promised to remain His faithful soldier and servant for ever.

Ralph Hutton had been the head boy of Harrowton school, the schoolmaster's right hand, and the good Vicar's favourite chorister. There had never been a single complaint against the lad,—no one in all the village ever said one word against young Ralph. And when he left his home at last, to be bound apprentice to a cabinet-maker in a distant town, every one was sorry to lose him—every one bade him GOD speed, and said how glad they should be to welcome him back to the old place.

But from that day to the day on which our story begins, Ralph had never returned to Harrowton. His father and mother died during the first year of his apprenticeship, his elder brother went to Australia, his sister married. The poor lad had no home, and he lived on in his master's house in Broxham, amongst companions who laughed at him for what they called his methodistical ways, and tried to set him against all he had been taught to love and reverence.

If you had asked the Harrowton folk to tell you the distinguishing feature of Ralph Hutton's character, they would in all probability have answered, "his dauntless courage." He was brave and fearless as a young lion, enterprising almost to rashness, and yet deep down in his heart, hidden from mortal eye, known only to himself and to his GOD, there lurked a fault—ay, may we not call it a sin?—which in his pride and self-confidence he did not strive to struggle against, and which brought him untold misery as time went on.

Brave, fearless, Ralph was deficient in moral courage. He would face any danger, combat any difficulty; but he could not bear to be laughed at—he could not stand ridicule.

And so, when his companions laughed at him for going to Church regularly, and kneeling down, and saying his prayers in his room, he felt awkward and uncomfortable. He did not do what he ought to have done—what all of us must do in the little trials of our daily life—he did not ask GOD to strengthen him in his weakness, and to make him bear taunts and ridicule patiently for His dear sake, Who for our sakes was mocked and scourged and spit upon, and Who answered not a word, but bore all that He had voluntarily taken upon Himself, bowed His meek Head in all things to His heavenly FATHER's will.

Ralph did not give up all he had been taught at once. Only step by step, little by little, he left off the good old ways; he went through back streets to Church on Sundays, as if he were doing something he was ashamed of; and he waited till the lights were out to say his prayers, so that the two lads who shared his bedroom might not see what he was doing; and then by degrees he fell into careless ways, and his companions, who were a wicked, lawless set, had more discernment than the Harrowton folk : they saw the weak point in the boy's character, and took advantage of it.

The youth himself was very unhappy in those days—very lonely and miserable. He did not remember the words the good old Vicar had spoken to him the last time he was with him, in · that dear old home which now could never be home to him any more.

" Ralph, my son, I know it's hard for you to go out into the world, but try and remember all you promised at your Confirmation and first Communion : try and be true and pure in all things, in thought and word and deed.

" Remember your Guardian Angel will ever be at your side, unless you drive him away by un-resisted sin. You will fall often, Ralph ; we all of us fall daily and hourly. We were sent into the world to fight and to wrestle against the powers of darkness, against sin, the world, and the devil. We are soldiers, my boy, every one of us, soldiers of the Cross ; and what should you think of a soldier who said he could not fight the battles of his country? You may be lonely, Ralph, in your new life, you may long for home and your friends sometimes, it is but right and natural that you should do so; but even amid your loneliness you will be quite happy, if you keep near, very near to GOD, and ask Him to strengthen you in the strife, and to be with you, and help you, and raise you when you fall."

No, poor Ralph remembered none of this : his Guardian Angel spoke to him, only to be disregarded ; conscience whispered to him, only that he might stifle its warning, pleading voice.

He was just twenty years of age when quite accidentally he met an old Harrowton friend,—a girl named Jinny Grey, who had got a situation as maid of all work in a tradesman's family in Broxham. The Greys had been noted in Harrowton as a thriftless careless set, the father and mother were idle and inclined to drink, the children were neglected, and suffered to do pretty much as they liked. Jinny, the youngest of ten, was the most hopeful amongst them all : she was a bright, pretty little thing, and Ralph Hutton had always noticed her, and spoken a kind word to her as she trudged to and from the village school to her wretched home.

When he saw her in Broxham, it seemed like a bit of the old life coming to him amidst his wretchedness; he would meet her on Sunday evenings, and walk out into the country with her, and talk of former days, and of his dead father and mother; and she seemed so glad to be with him, and looked so pretty in her Sunday attire, (although Ralph in his heart thought it a great deal too gaudy and very unlike the way in which the good old Vicar liked the Harrowton maidens to dress,) that one day he told her that he thought they had better be married and see whether they should not get on together. They were both lonely and miserable, and he thought it was the best thing they could do.

Jinny thought so too; so it was all settled, and the wedding day was fixed; and the wedding took place one chill November day; and Ralph took his bride to her new home;—but they neither of them asked GOD's blessing upon the life upon which they had just entered; neither of them ever went to Church or to Holy Communion, or put into practice what they had been taught all those years ago in Harrowton.

One bright Sunday morning in June, Jinny had said to her husband, "Could we not go to Church to-day, Ralph?"

"Do as you like," was the answer, "I ain't a-going to make a spectacle of myself in these clothes; and besides, it wouldn't do us any good; you'd only come home to say hard things to me, and to nag at me," and Ralph laughed a harsh discordant laugh, and looked round the dreary, dirty room, with an expression upon his face different, oh, so different, to the bright, winning look which had won all hearts in the olden days.

Jinny sighed wearily; she had been happy enough at first, Ralph had been very kind to her in the first days of their married life; but, poor thing, her own home had not been a good school in which to learn to be a tidy, thrifty housewife, and Ralph would come from his day's work to a dirty, untidy room, and he would grumble and lament his marriage, and say that he was more comfortable in the old days when he lived in his master's house.

And Jinny, instead of trying to make things better, would only grumble too, and lament her hard fate, and wish she were back in the trades-man's house, scrubbing and cleaning from morn-ing till night. She had never known what it was to be patient and gentle; she had always allowed herself to speak the thoughts that came uppermost, and now she did nothing but rail and storm at poor Ralph, making his home so miserable that it was hardly to be wondered at that he sought refuge at the Hen and Chickens.

Sometimes longings for better things came to her; she used to wish that the old days when she had gone to Church regularly, and said her prayers, would come back again; but she did not seek to bring them back,—she only thought and longed, she did not act.

She sat on, on that Sunday morning when Ralph had refused to go to Church with her, and a tear stood in her eye, for she had heard him bang the door, and greet some of his companions in the street,—some young men who she knew bore a very bad character in the place.

The church bells rang merrily on, and still poor Jinny sat in the wretched room, and a dull dead weight was upon her heart.

She grew tired and weary of doing nothing, and then she took a Prayer Book down from the shelf,—oh, how dusty it was, it had not been used for so long,—and she turned to the Collect and Epistle and Gospel for the day,—the Fifth Sunday after Trinity. It was the words of the Epistle that came home to the poor sorrowful young wife: "Be ye all of one mind, having compassion one of another; love as brethren, be pitiful, be courteous; not rendering evil for evil,

or railing for railing, but contrariwise blessing."

Poor Jinny, she remembered how she had
once heard the old Vicar at home preach a
sermon upon those very words, " Be pitiful, be
courteous ;" and how he had said that if we did
not show compassion to others GOD would show
none to us.

" I will try and be kinder to Ralph," she
mused ; but she did not ask GOD to help her to
be kind, and so her resolutions were like a house
built upon the sand, and when the first wind of
temptation came, they fell to the ground.

That night when Ralph returned to his home
with a bright light in his eye, and a flush upon
his cheek, which told their own tale, he found
an old neighbour sitting with his wife, and a
poor puny baby lay by Jinny's side.

" I am very sorry," began Ralph.

" Don't make any excuses for yourself, Ralph
Hutton, as you always try to do, 'tain't of no
avail, but mark my words : unless you and your
missis mends your ways,—for there's faults on
both sides,—you with your liking for gay companions, and she with her carelessness, and her
grumbling and fault-finding, trouble will come

to you, as sure as my name's Betsy Baker,—
you've both of you been better taught, lad, and
GOD finds out the way to bring them as has
once known Him back to Him again, but most
times it's through a deal of sorrow and pain.
But He don't send it all at once, Ralph Hutton;
He calls you by gentle ways first, He is calling
you to-night, you and your wife, by the gift He
has sent you, by the blessing He has given you
in that poor little unconscious child."

The old woman's tones were strangely earnest,
she spoke like one who had known the sin and
the sorrow of which she spoke, like one who
was trying to warn and to teach another out of
her own most bitter experience; and Ralph did
not resent her plain speaking; on the contrary,
some strange far away memories of his own
childhood, and of the father and mother he had
loved so well, came to him there, and he stooped
down and kissed the poor little baby, and gazed
lovingly at his sleeping wife.

"I will be a better man," he mused; "I will
go to Church and try to do as the good old
Vicar at home told me to do; and I must be a
good husband to Jinny, and a good father to the
little one."

He was quite sober now, and he meant every

word he said, but he trusted in his own strength, he did not ask GOD to help him to keep his newly-formed resolutions.

Jinny was very weak and ill for a long time, and Ralph was very patient and gentle with her; he and old Betsy Baker took the child to Church and had it baptised by the name of Mary; the poor little thing seemed gradually to be pining away, and the old woman never rested until it was made GOD's own little one.

The first Sunday that Jinny could go out Ralph gave her his arm, and they walked to Church together, and were very proud and happy, and agreed that it should be the beginning of better things; but somehow even then they did not seem to remember that GOD alone could help them in their trials and difficulties; and they never thought or spoke of that most Holy Communion of which they had both learned as a means of grace which GOD has provided for His creatures.

No! on Sunday mornings when in the silence and stillness of the early morning hour GOD's minister administered the Holy Food, Jinny and Ralph lay fast asleep in their bed; unheeding the gracious call spoken by CHRIST Himself to those who would inherit Eternal Life.

Weeks and months passed on; the little sickly baby lived, but certainly did not thrive, and Betsy Baker saw that things were growing worse and worse, and Ralph had gone back to his old companions, and Jinny to her grumbling ways; and the old woman felt that somehow or other her words would come true, and that it would take some great sorrow or trouble to bring the two poor things into the ways from which they had so erred and strayed.

The wretched home grew more and more wretched; it was in vain that Betsy spoke—in vain that she remonstrated, it seemed as if nothing could be done, no one can help those who do not help themselves. So, poor old woman, she did the only thing which all of us can do for our neighbours, she prayed for them; and she tried to teach little Mary to be a loving gentle child.

The little one spent most of her time in Betsy's room; she had grown into a little pale sallow girl with a prematurely old expression upon her face, and a look of intense suffering upon her baby brow. And the little Mary did suffer very very much; when she was but a year old, an abscess had formed in her hip, and it had never healed, and the poor little thing was a helpless cripple.

Other children were born to Ralph and Jinny, but they all died young, and only Mary was left to them, her little ringing voice was the only joyous sound that was ever heard in that wretched room which was the Huttons' home.

For in spite of the look of suffering upon her poor little face, Mary was very bright and happy sometimes; only the tears would start into her soft brown eyes, and the little lips would quiver, when father and mother said hard words to each other, and when father threatened to go away.

With all the intensity of her loving earnest nature Mary loved her father, and her love was returned by him. She was the one bright spot in his cheerless life, the one thing left to him that seemed to bring back to him his happy innocent boyhood; for her sake he would sometimes stay at home of an evening, for her sake he would give up the companions who lured him from his home, and he would patiently endure the sight of the comfortless room, from which each article of furniture was disappearing by degrees, and hear Jinny's grumbling, that he might sit with his little one on his knee, and listen to her innocent prattle.

There came a cold hard winter when Mary was seven years old, which brought misery and starvation to her home in Broxham; and work was scarce, and wages were low, and discontent was rife amongst those who had wives and children crying for bread at home, and who had none to give them.

And it was on an evening during this hard winter that Ralph Hutton spoke the words with which our story opens, and thinking only of his grumbling wife and his miserable home, and forgetting the soft loving eyes which even then were gazing anxiously down the narrow lane to "watch for father," made up his mind to smoke his pipe in the bar of the Hen and Chickens.

There was a stormy discussion going on that night amongst some of the disaffected workmen.

Ralph had long ago left his old trade, and had got employment at some iron works in the neighbourhood, and the men who were speaking, and ranting, and raving against their employer, who was the kindest master whom workmen could have, were his comrades and associates.

He had often heard them so speak before, but to do him justice he had never listened to their wild and senseless words; now, however, as he sat in the chimney corner silent and gloomy, one of them addressed him, and tempted him to join in their schemes.

"We shall have a meeting at midnight when the house is quiet; Hutton, they say you're a clever chap, and a scholar, will you address us, will you put our wrongs before us? not that we don't know them well enough, but there's nothing like eloquence to stir up one's courage, and you're the very fellow to do it if all they say of you is true."

Again Ralph's Guardian Angel spoke to him, and bade him not to be led into temptation; but he had disregarded the warning voice of GOD's own messenger all through those long years; he hardly understood the soft gentle whispers now, which spoke to him in a voice that sounded like the voice of his child.

There was a moment's pause, an instant's irresolution.

"Your hand on it, old fellow," said the voice of Ralph's tempter; (and in the loud coarse tones, the sweet sound of that other low whisper was completely drowned.) "Your hand on it, say that you are our man."

And Ralph, poor misguided Ralph, held out his hand, and promised to wait for that midnight meeting, which was to rid the working men of their toils and oppressions.

With that meeting, however, we have nought

to do; long speeches were made, long debates followed, and Ralph Hutton spoke eloquently and described in pathetic language the (so-called) wrongs of the sons of toil; and the poor infatuated fellows, Ralph amongst them, drank long and deeply, and then they came to a desperate resolution. They agreed to burn down their master's house in the silence and darkness of the winter's night.

And Ralph, daring, courageous, fearless as of old, was to lead them on to the commission of the foul deed.

Little Mary was suffering very much that night. Hour after hour she kept her weary watch at the window, but father did not come home, and the tears coursed each other down her little pale cheeks, and her mother spoke crossly to her, and bade her pull down the tattered blind, and come to bed.

"Mother, the pain is so bad I don't think I can sleep, and it hurts me so much to lie down; may I wait until father comes home?"

"No, I'm tired and worn out, child, and I've not had a mouthful between my lips this day; there's nothing but to try and go to sleep and forget my misery, and I ain't going to have you making a noise and disturbing me, so come and lie down at once."

The child obeyed. Obedience had been one of the lessons taught her by old Betsy Baker; she too was tired and hungry, and in addition to this the poor diseased hip was more than usually painful; but Mary, as she lay on the hard bed thought of the cold manger which had been the cradle of the Holy Child JESUS, and she said some hymns to herself, and in her hand she held a little wooden cross which always hung round her neck, and which old Betsy had got her grandson, who was a carpenter, to make for the child, and she told her that if she thought of the suffering JESUS bore for her it would help her to bear the pain that GOD sent her because He loved her.

The little one was thinking of some of the words she had heard in Church, (for Betsy always took her godchild to Church,) and .how the clergyman had told the children, at their own especial service, that JESUS, the Child JESUS, sent them trouble and sorrow because He loved them, and wished to make them like Himself, and with these holy comforting thoughts in her mind, little Mary fell asleep.

She awoke at last, the sharp pain would not

allow of her having many hours' rest at once, and she thought it must be morning, for a strange light shone into the room, and lit up her sleeping mother's face; and yet it was not like the gradual dawning of the winter's day.

This light was red and bright, and played in strange fantastic shadows on the wall; and suddenly, as Mary watched it, there came a sudden fear into her mind. She got up hurriedly and crawled to the window; she would not use her crutch for fear of wakening her mother, and she saw people rushing hurriedly along the street, eager, anxious, and excited, and from afar sounded strange cries, and she thought she heard the words "fire—fire."

Then from the old Church tower the bells sounded, and Mary knew that something dreadful had happened; and she sat shivering and trembling, for "father" was out and "mother" was asleep, and there was no one to speak one word of comfort to the poor little girl.

Then she knelt upon the cold floor, and asked GOD to take care of her, and of father and mother, and old Betsy Baker, and again the poor weary child fell asleep upon the hard boards, with an old wooden footstool for a pillow.

When she awoke again, the strange light had disappeared; the faint gleam of dawn which tells that a winter's day is breaking stole into the room, and Mary knew that another day had come, and that "father" was still away. .

She sat on in the cold with the shadow of a nameless fear upon her poor little heart, and when another hour afterwards old Betsy appeared in the doorway pale and trembling, and with a strange pitying look in her dear grey eyes, Mary said in a quiet unnatural tone,

"What has happened to father, Granny?"

"Bless the child, what have you heard?"

"Nothing,—but the pain has been very bad all night, and I could not sleep much,—and I saw a red light, and I got up and looked out, and there were so many people in the street, and they called out 'fire,' and father's not come home, and I'm afraid."

"My poor lamb, my poor dear suffering lamb," was the old woman's only answer, and she took the little one in her arms and tried to soothe her, and then Jinny awoke startled and bewildered, and asked what it all meant.

"Jinny Hutton, I'd be the last to bring my words up against you now, for my heart is very sore, and GOD knows it is, for you and my pre-

:ious little lamb; but the great trouble, as I
.lways felt sure must come, has come now,
`inny, my dear, it's no use to try and hide it
:om you. The iron works and the master's
1ouse was set on fire last night by some of the
rorkmen, and burned to the ground; them who
iid it has been took up, and Ralph is one of
hem,—they say as how he was the first to light
he match."

Then Jinny bowed her head upon her hands,
nd said,

"Oh, Betsy, Betsy, it's my hard words and
rumbling as has drove him to this."

And Betsy Baker somehow or other hoped
hat all the trouble and disgrace might be the
.awning of brighter days.

Ralph and his companions were tried, and
entenced to six months' imprisonment with
ard labour; it was only at the intervention
f the master whom they had so cruelly
ronged that so light a sentence was passed
n them.

Those winter days were very hard days for
1e mother and child. Little Mary was very ill,
nd at one time Jinny feared that she would
ie.

"It would break his heart," she said to Betsy
Baker, "not to see the child again."

GOD in His mercy spared her. Ralph Hutton
left the prison at the end of six months, and
went to his old home longing to see his darling,
but trembling at the thought of the torrent of
angry words with which Jinny was sure to greet
him. He stood in the doorway hardly daring
to enter, and yet longing to hold little Mary in
his arms once more.

"Ralph," said Jinny, "dear Ralph, I have
asked GOD to teach me to be gentle and compassionate."

And Ralph could only sob like a child and
say, "And I will do my best to be good to you."

Those who know Ralph Hutton and his wife
now are never tired of telling of their goodness
and their happiness. They are always at Church
always at Holy Communion; and although little
Mary is still very ill and suffers very much, the
sunshine of GOD's love rests upon that humble
home, and Betsy Baker sometimes says that
Jinny has a fault now it is that she is too yield-
ing and gentle. "For the men does require
keeping in order, my dear, especially when they
comes in with dirty boots."

And Jinny answers softly, "When I don't
do nothing worse than come in with dirty boots,
Granny, I'll begin to scold my Ralph."

"Speak gently! it is better far
   To rule by love than fear ;
Speak gently! let not harsh words mar
   The good we might do here.

"Speak gently to the little child,
   Its love be sure to gain :
Teach it in accents soft and mild,
   It may not long remain.

"Speak gently to the young, for they
   Will have enough to bear ;
Pass through this life as best they may,
   'Tis full of anxious care.

"Speak gently to the aged one,
   Grieve not the careworn heart ;
The sands of life are nearly run,
   Let such in peace depart.

"Speak gently, kindly to the poor,
   Let no harsh word be heard !
They have enough they must endure,
   Without an unkind word.

"Speak gently ! 'tis a little thing
  Dropped in the heart's deep well ;
The good, the joy that it may bring,
  Eternity shall tell."

THROUGH THE SHADOWS.

Sixth Sunday after Trinity.

"Through cloud and sunshine, LORD, abide with me."

IT was a July day, bright and warm and sunny, and the boys of Wrangerton school were standing idly in the playground, trying to decide what game they had better play during the quarter of an hour that must elapse before school would begin.

The hot weather had somehow or other upset all their plans; they had meant to practise for a grand race that was to come off some time after the holidays, which by the way were to begin before another week had passed away; but, as they very justly remarked, no one *could* race under such a burning sun as was beating on their heads that day; so they had

v.   C

given up the idea, and stood about talking and laughing, and sad to say in one or two cases, disputing.

Wrangerton school had been established for centuries,—it had been founded by an old Lord De Courcy, who all his life long had been a great miser, and who at his death had left all that he had to various charities,—the principal part of his enormous income however had gone to the foundation of a school for the sons of professional men, but it was necessary that the boys to be educated at Wrangerton must have lost both or at least one of their parents, so that the institution was really an orphanage, but it was never called by that name.

To those, however, who knew the rules of Wrangerton school there was something of sadness in the sight of the bright young faces of the boys—(for the most part their faces were very bright)—for it was impossible to help feeling that sorrow, as yet perhaps unknown and unfelt, had clouded the lives of those poor children, that a mother's tender loving care had been withdrawn from them, or that a father's firm strong hand no longer kept them in check, and showed them the best way of fighting the battle of life.

But we are just glancing at the dark side of the picture; for the most part those Wrangerton boys were as merry a set of lads as you could wish to find; and generally the sound of their blithe young voices in the playground was undisturbed by any discordant tones of anger or of passion.

On that July afternoon on which my story begins, there were, as I have already said, one or two disputants amongst that noisy merry group.

Let us play the eavesdropper, and listen to what two of those boys are saying, whilst one or two others who are standing near, catch the echo of the angry, sinful words.

"I saw you looking over Elkington's book, and I know you were cribbing, and it isn't fair, you know it isn't, Bligh."

"Say it again, and I'll knock you down," answered Bligh, his cheeks flushed with passion.

There was no reply; Bligh's accuser stood before him, a pale, gentle looking boy, by name Walter Thurlow, and only a very slight tinge of colour was on his face as he raised his dark eyes fearlessly, and looked straight at his antagonist.

"Bligh," he said at last, "don't be angry,
I'm not going to tell, I'd rather be flayed alive
than peach, at least just now,—but you know
how wrong it is, you know I'm head of the division, and it wouldn't be right of me to see the
prize taken away from Elkington, because you've
been dis—dis—dishonourable."

With a mighty effort the obnoxious word
came out, and poor Walter's lip quivered, and
his voice trembled as he pronounced it.

"Dishonourable! you dare to use such an
expression towards me! I could have stood it
from any other fellow in the school, I cannot
and will not stand it from you."

This time there was a burning blush on Walter's pale cheek; he knew too well why it was
that Rupert Bligh would not stand such a word
spoken by him; he knew that the boy was the
only person in all the school who knew that the
stain of dire life-long disgrace was on his name;
and yet he could not and would not withdraw
the accusation.

It was the custom in Wrangerton school to
appoint one of the boys to be head of a division,
and to be answerable as far as he could for the
behaviour of the boys thus placed under his
care.

Bligh and Elkington were trying for the same prize, and it so happened that Walter had caught the former cribbing from the latter's verses. It was a well-known fact that Elkington had the best chance of success, and shy, timid Walter had made up his mind that he *must* speak,—but oh, how he had dreaded it; how he had put it off all through the bright summer's day, and how gently he had tried to say it at last.

He had said a little prayer, and asked GOD to help him to do what was right; and now, as he stood there listening to Bligh's taunting words, he again asked for strength to bear whatever should be said, for he knew quite well what was coming; he was not in the least surprised when he heard his companion say, " *You* talk to any one else of being dishonourable, *you*, the forger's son !"

He bowed his head, poor lad, in very shame, for he knew how true the accusation was; he remembered what he had felt on that autumn afternoon now nearly a year ago, when he had turned round at a whisper from one of his companions as he was standing in class, to look at the new boy; and the new boy proved to be Rupert Bligh, the doctor's son, from Cardington, the town where Walter had lived all his life until

two years ago, when he had come to Wrangerton,
with an old maiden aunt of his mother's.

He had heard that Dr. Bligh was dead, and
he supposed that this accounted for Rupert's
appearance at Wrangerton. He only knew the
boy by sight. In fact, Walter had never mixed
with any lads of his own age in his old home,—
there had always been that terrible stain of disgrace upon his name, and Aunt Judith had tried
to shield him as best she could from the taunts
and sneering remarks of those around him.

It had all happened when he was a very little
boy; he could just remember a dark, gloomy
winter's day, when the old Vicar came in and
told his mother something that made her cry
very bitterly. She was lying on the sofa very
ill then, and she never went outside the doors
again but once, and that was when a carriage
from the Dolphin came and took her away.
Sarah, the old servant, told Walter that she was
going to wish his father good-bye before he went
over the seas.

The boy had never cared for his father; all
the love of his childish heart had been centred
upon his loving gentle mother.

"She is not going over the seas too, is she?"
he asked.

"No, no, my dear," answered the faithful old servant; and then she turned away, and Walter heard her murmur, "She's going a longer journey than that, I'm thinking, poor weary, patient soul."

In the days that were to come Walter never forgot those words : he saw his mother come home from that farewell visit, to her husband in the county jail, paler, thinner, sadder, than she had ever been before ; he remembered all through his young life, how she had clasped him in her arms, and told him that he was her only comfort, and he had asked her if she was going on a journey, because Sarah had said she was, and she had smiled a smile that had in it something of joy as she answered, "If it were not for you, my darling, I would fain go ; and even as it is, surely they would be kind to you, my little innocent Walter."

"Mother, dear, dear mother, don't go,—promise me you won't go."

"Not until God in His own good time sends for me to go home, my darling."

The days passed on, and one summer's evening the mother called her boy to her side and said,

"Walter, God has sent for me ; join your little

hands, my darling, and say, Please GOD, help mother on her long dark journey."

He said that little prayer a great many times, and then Sarah took him away and put him to bed; and in the morning Aunt Judith led him into the room where his mother lay, all still and white upon her bed; all covered with lovely flowers. And the old lady told the child that in that country whither his mother had journeyed flowers more beautiful than any he had ever seen always grew, and angels sang sweet songs of joy for ever and for ever.

After that, Walter had gone home to Aunt Judith's old house at the other end of the town, and there he had lived until the day when with the blinding tears standing in her dim old eyes, she had bade him good-bye, and sent him off to that strange new life at Wrangerton.

He had learned all the sad story of his father's sin long before that,—bit by bit it had come to him that Walter Thurlow the elder had been a forger, and was now a felon; bit by bit it dawned upon him what that secret grief had been that had killed his gentle mother; bit by bit the tender sensitive nature had realised what it was that made him different to other children, that made Aunt Judith so cross, and so angry if he spoke to the little boys and girls in the street, and tried to make friends with them.

She had never spoken to him of his father; she never knew how much of the bitter tale had come within the childish ken, only when Walter had stood pale and trembling upon the door-step he had turned to her, and said in a scarcely audible voice,

"Aunt Judith, do they know about it there?"

"About what, Walter?"

"About my—, about that that happened ever so long ago before she went away."

Then poor old Aunt Judith understood that all the care she had taken to keep her boy from the knowledge of the stain that was upon his name had been unavailing.

"No, my dear, no one knows, except the head master," she answered, "you need not be afraid, Walter, Wrangerton is a very long way off, and no one there ever will know."

And so the poor little fellow had gone away reassured, and he had got on very well, and was at the head of his class, and took home such a good character to Aunt Judith at the end of each term; and he was more bright and merry than he had ever been in all his life before; it seemed as though the shadow that had fallen upon his early childhood was passing away, and giving place to the sunny cheerfulness of a happy laughter-loving schoolboy.

Something of the shadow came back the day that Rupert Bligh appeared in the Wrangerton schoolroom, but the new comer did not seem inclined to revert in any way to the past, and time passed on, and Walter forgot his fears, and it was only on that July afternoon when my story begins that the crushing fact came back to him, and he knew that he, the forger's son, would be disgraced in the sight of all his school-fellows.

He stood there in the sunshine, his head bowed, his hands clenched, the cold big drops of agony starting to his brow, knowing that he could not deny the accusation, and yet feeling that he could not stay there and bear it.

One or two of the boys were, as I have told you, standing near, and caught the echo of Rupert's words.

"A forger's son," shouted one of them; "who is that, Bligh? tell us about it."

"There he stands," answered Bligh proudly and angrily; "I should never have said it, if he had not accused me of being dishonourable."

At that moment the school bell rang. Walter

waited to hear no more; he could not face the boys, could not bear all those eyes scanning the face of the forger's son; he turned out of the great gates, and walked along the dusty high road; he knew not, cared not whither it might lead him, anything to get off, anything to escape that dreaded schoolboy scrutiny, to be away from the fierce ordeal of questions which he knew would be put to him.

He could not think then, he could not pray. He forgot how only the day before he had knelt at the Altar of GOD, and had received strength for every trial, in the most holy Sacrament of CHRIST'S Body and Blood. Hatred and anger were in his heart; the words too of the Blessed JESUS, which he had heard in the Gospel, (that for the Sixth Sunday after Trinity,) were all unheeded now, "Whosoever hateth his brother shall be in danger of the judgment." He had thought of all these things very much only one short day before, now they had gone from his mind, and the poor weary, tired, excited boy walked on and on and on, until at last, worn out and exhausted by the heat, and by all those terribly conflicting feelings, he lay down by the roadside and fell fast asleep.

When he awoke the cool evening breeze was

blowing upon his fevered brow, and by his side stood a recruiting sergeant, dressed in a bright red coat, and with ever so many different coloured ribbons flowing from his cap.

"Hullo, youngster, what do you say to being a soldier?" he said in a cheery voice to poor Walter.

"I don't know, sir."

"Don't know—then who is to know? you're a likely lad enough; you could write to your father and mother, and tell them you was off to foreign lands."

Walter's face brightened at the suggestion,— to get away far from those who knew his story appeared his one chance of happiness and success.

"I have no father,—at least he is a long, long way off,—and my mother is dead; there is only poor old Aunt Judith at Cardington, I cannot leave her."

"O yes, you can, she'll be proud of her soldier nephew; the old gals always like the red coats, and you can go home to her in two or three years, and tell her of all the grand things you have seen, and take her a bird of paradise to stick into her turban."

"She doesn't wear a turban," answered Walter, half indignant at Aunt Judith being laughed at by this stranger, who seemed so very free and easy, and yet was so provokingly good-natured with it all.

"Doesn't she? more's the pity; well, you'll be able to take her all the money you will have earned."

"Shall I earn money?" asked poor Walter eagerly and hopefully.

"I should think you would, my lad, a power of it; why, if we goes to the wars there's no telling how rich we may not all be when we come home."

"I will go," answered Walter; "I want to be rich, I don't want to be a burden to Aunt Judith, and I cannot, I dare not go back to school."

Before the evening of another day Walter was in barracks in a large garrison town in the south of England. He heard that the regiment which he had joined was under orders for foreign service, and he wrote a short note to poor old Aunt Judith.

"MY DEAR AUNT,—Bligh twitted me with it, and I couldn't bear it; I know I ought to have stopped at school, and to have borne it all, because of all that our Blessed LORD bore for our sakes; and when I came here last night I remembered all you had taught me, and I was very sorry I had been so hasty, but it would have prevented my doing any work to know all that the fellows would have said, and to know that it was all true, and I should not have got on, and I should only have been a burden to you, and now I am going away to be a soldier. Our regiment starts next week for the Mediterranean, and perhaps there may be war somewhere or other,—the sergeant said there would be,—and I will get a lot of prize money, and come home and bring it all to you; don't fret, dear, dear Aunt Judith, only please give my love to Sarah, and accept the same from

" Your very affectionate nephew,

" WALTER THURLOW."

It was a good thing that the poor lad did not see the agony that was upon the old face he loved so well, when Aunt Judith read the simple words which told her that her darling had gone from her. He had, as he said, begun to see that he had done wrongly in running away from that grievous trouble; doubtless it would have been more brave and soldier-like to face it out, and yet it was a hard and bitter trial, and the boy was young and timid, and sensitive, and GOD saw into that poor little aching heart, and in His infinite love and compassion for the weakness that shrank from suffering, surely He forgave the motherless, and worse than fatherless boy.

In the days and months and years that came afterwards, Walter repented more bitterly than ever, of the rash deed he had committed on that July afternoon. He was a studious, clever, thoughtful boy, and books and study seemed to be his natural element, whilst in his new bustling active soldier's life there was little time, and still less opportunity for reading and study.

But the discipline was good for him; better perhaps than the dreaming over old folios would have been. The lad's character strengthened beneath the ordinary, monotonous routine, of his daily duties; and at last one day, when he had been at Gibraltar for about four years, his colonel sent for him, and asked him if he would like his discharge.

"You have been looking pale and thin lately, Thurlow," he said, "and perhaps you had better get home to your people. I don't think the life you are leading is a very fitting one for you, although you have done your duty in it nobly. I have arranged everything for you, if you will go back to England; I wrote to the authorities at home some time ago, and I have the offer of a clerkship in the War Office for you."

It was quite true that Walter had been ailing for a long time, and now when the hope of going home again and seeing Aunt Judith came to him, he could hardly bear the joy, it seemed almost too great. And then there came a cloud to overshadow it: would his story follow him to the War Office, as it had followed him to school?

He told the colonel his fears.

"Don't look out for evil, Thurlow; only if it comes, don't run away from it again. Bear it bravely and patiently, as a soldier, and as a Christian should."

So it was all settled, and ere another month had passed, Walter was sitting on a footstool at Aunt Judith's feet in the old house at Cardington, just as he had sat all those years ago when he was a little boy.

He was talking of the past, and of the faraway school days. He hardly reverted to the cause of all the trouble; it was too painful a subject to be discussed, even to the dear old aunt.

"Where is Bligh?" he asked, at last; "did he ever come back to the old place again? You said in one of your letters that his mother had gone away."

"Yes, he came back, soon after you left,—he was expelled from Wrangerton. He was found out in something that neither the master nor the boys could brook, and he came home in disgrace, and nearly broke his poor old mother's heart. I hear he is getting on well in London now; but Mrs. Bligh died more than two years ago, and I think somehow that Rupert's conduct hastened her end."

There came into Walter's heart a strange triumphant feeling; after all he had been right in those old Wrangerton days. Rupert was a sneak, and dishonourable,—all in fact, and perhaps more than he had ever thought him,—and it was because of this boy's accusations that he had run away from school. He knew now that he should not have heeded them—he had known it for a very long time—but he had never felt as he felt on that evening, when Aunt Judith told him of Rupert's disgrace; never knew until then, what it was to glory in another's shame.

He said his prayers before he went to bed. He had never missed saying them morning and evening all through his soldier's life, and he knelt at the holy altar the next Sunday, and all those wrong, angry, revengeful feelings were in his heart.

A few days more, and he was in London, happy and content to a certain extent in his new occupation, and yet with a strange weight upon him, which he had never felt before. He did not know what it was then,—did not fathom the depths of his soul, and see that down deep, hidden from human eye, but seen by the Searcher of all hearts was the cherished feeling of mingled hatred and triumph, against Rupert Bligh.

He was popular enough in his office—unusually so, indeed, for a youth who had been there so short a time; and some of his companions asked him to their houses to dinner, and the old shadow had gone quite away now. He never as much as thought of the stain upon his name during all the months that followed his arrival in town.

There was one of the clerks in Walter's room to whom he had from the first taken a great dislike; in fact, there was not one of all the juniors who had a good word to say for Frank Lawson.

The seniors said he was steady at his work; but even they did not seem prepossessed in favour of the dark, cynical looking youth, who always seemed to be watching every one from beneath those dark bushy eyebrows of his.

" Thurlow," he said one day, fixing his steady gaze upon Walter's face, ·· Thurlow, your name is an uncommon one, you don't happen to be any relative of a man who was transported some twelve or fourteen years ago for forgery? I know a fellow, Rupert Bligh his name is, and I was talking about you, and he told me just to ask you the question."

"Ask Rupert why he was——" began poor Walter, turning deadly pale, and then he stopped. He was going to say, "why he was expelled from Wrangerton," but the youth's Guardian Angel was near him then, and the unmanly speech never reached the ears of him for whom it was meant.

Again Lawson spoke. " I asked for no message for Bligh; I only wanted an answer to a simple question from yourself—was that man your father or not?"

" He was, but it can be no business of yours;" and Walter took his hat from its peg, and walked quickly away, for it was a Saturday afternoon, and just time to shut up, when the cowardly taunt had been hurled at the poor fellow's head.

He never knew how he spent that half holiday. He wandered out beyond Stoke Newington Green, and found himself on Stamford Hill, and then when night came on he walked back to his lodgings, and he took up a book that Aunt Judith had given him, and read the meditation for the Sixth Sunday after Trinity, for it was the eve of that Sunday upon which all this misery had come to him.

He remembered how it was this very Gospel that he had heard in the old Church at Wrangerton, on the Sunday before the first great blow had been dealt him, and it seemed strange that the lesson of forgiveness should come to him again now.

" I will go to Church to-morrow morning," he said, to the Blessed Sacrament, " I shall find help and peace there." And then he began to read Aunt Judith's old book.

" My children, the gift that you are supposed to bring to the Holy Altar is yourselves, all your whole hearts, to be a reasonable, holy, and living Sacrifice unto God. And when you come to Church, when you kneel in the Sacred Presence of the Lord of all love, if you remember that your brother has aught against you, that is, if you have at any time wronged any one by thought, word, or deed, you must not presume to draw near to your LORD in this His Sacrament of Love; you must leave your gift before the Altar—the gift of repentance for all the angry feelings you may have cherished against another; you must go and be reconciled to him, and then come back and be made one with Him, Who forgave and prayed for His murderers. My children, so many '*aughts*' can be brought against all of us; it may be that we too have ' aughts' to bring against others—with these we have nothing to do to-day. I don't think we ever have anything to do with them, it is only of our own short-comings that we must think—we *must* be reconciled to those not only to whom we have done wrong, but to those of whom we have had angry revengeful thoughts, before we can come to the Blessed Eucharistic Feast."

Walter read the words, and it seemed as though a mist had fallen from his eyes, and he saw clearly all the sin of which he had been guilty for months; he knew now what that was which had lain like a weight upon his heart for so long.

Even as he was thinking how he could be reconciled to his brothers—to Rupert who had so sorely injured him, and to Frank Lawson, whom he had felt that day as if he would like to kill. There was the sound of a light springy footstep upon the stairs, and Beaumont, one of his particular friends, entered the room without as much as knocking, looking very grave.

"Dear old fellow, I have been here half a dozen times just to tell you that we like you all the better, because of this afternoon, but that's not what I've come for now; hasn't that fellow Bligh a sister down in your part of the world?"

"Yes, Mrs. Webster."

"Very well; send a telegram to her, and tell her to come at once; her brother and Lawson have been thrown out of a dog-cart, and there's not much hope for either of them. I was passing Charing Cross at the time and saw it all."

"Where are they?" asked Walter.

"At Lawson's lodgings."

"I will telegraph, and then I will go to them; once, when I was a soldier, I nursed a fellow who had had a bad accident."

"You, Thurlow, you come to them !"

"Yes, please don't say a word against it; I'll just run to the telegraph office, and you stay here a minute, and we'll have a glass of wine, and then go on to the poor fellows."

Whilst he was gone, Beaumont took up Aunt Judith's old book, and he knew why it was that his friend was going to Lawson's rooms that night.

When Walter came back there were tears in Beaumont's bright blue eyes, and he said, "Old fellow, it's all right, all as it should be."

"Thank GOD," was the low fervent answer; "I had made up my mind to go to them before you came in. Oh, Beaumont, what should I have done if they had died, without forgiving me?"

Beaumont did not answer; he understood what Walter meant, better than he would have done half an hour before.

Bligh and Lawson got well after weeks of suffering, and then the happiest day in all Walter's life was that day when Rupert told him that because of all he had done for them he and Lawson meant to go to Church, and lead better lives.

"It was not I, it was GOD."

"But GOD sent you to us, Walter, and because of the forgiveness you have granted us, we dare to hope for His."

The next bright day in our hero's life was mingled with a strange sadness, for it came in a letter from Australia, telling of his father's death —so humble and so penitent that the Priest who wrote it said, he had seldom known any one who had so redeemed the wasted years of his life.

" Tell my boy to think of me mercifully, and to pray for me still," such had been the convict's message to his son.

And Walter prays for his soul still; and he and Aunt Judith sit in the old house now, and Sarah says that the shadow has passed away from the young master's face.

And loving old Aunt Judith asks that her boy may walk safely through the shadows that may, ay, that must fall upon his earthly path until he shall reach the land "where shadows cease."

APPLE POLLY.

Seventh Sunday after Trinity.

"The gift of GOD is Eternal Life."

IN a well-known thoroughfare in the great city
of London, just at a corner where three or
four streets meet, there sits, and there has sat
for the last thirty years, an old shrivelled wizened
up woman, Polly by name,—familiarly called by
all her acquaintances " Apple Polly."

You can at once guess at the old woman's
trade ; she is a vendor of fruit ; nuts, oranges,
strawberries, all in their respective seasons are
to be found on Polly's stall, but apples are, so
to speak, her *specialité*, apples are the articles
upon which she prides herself, and it is as the
seller of the best apples ever to be found in

London outside Covent Garden that Polly's fame has gone forth to the world.

Winter and summer she is at her post; an umbrella which men who are old now say they have known as long as they have known Molly herself—(umbrellas must have been made of more durable material then than they are now)— is her shelter alike from rain and sun; alike in cold and heat Apple Polly sits at her corner, and people have learned to look upon her as a friend, and would be scarcely more astonished to find the Monument removed from its position than to miss the old woman from her stall.

She has a sharp tongue, some of the little street Arabs will tell you, ay, and a sharp hand too,—for many and many a hard blow has fallen upon the small black fists, and even sometimes upon the grimy faces of the urchins who infested Polly's stall, and who took advantage when her head was turned away of her supposed inability to see, and tried to help themselves to some of her tempting goods.

But somehow Polly *did* see, and it had become an accepted tradition among the small denizens of those city streets that the old apple woman had eyes behind her.

" Is they inside her shawl ?" one small boy

had said to his brother one day when he was informed of the astounding fact.

"Yes," answered the other, gravely, "I specks they must be, for nobody has ever seed them, and yet for sure they're somewhere."

It was a wholesome belief, and Polly found that she was reaping the advantage of it, in the smaller number of interlopers who surrounded her in hopes of being able to possess themselves of an occasional apple or orange, or still better, a tempting bunch of ripe red, shiny cherries.

And yet in spite of the stories that were current respecting the old woman's harshness, there were those who could tell many and many a tale of kindly deeds done by Apple Polly in her own strange way, deeds known to none but those who had been recipients of her charity, and to Him at Whose Feet they were laid by the recording angel to be written down in the Book of Life, against the lonely old woman's name.

For Apple Polly *was* very lonely,—once, ever so many years ago, she had had a loving husband and a little rosy child, but fever came to the house in which they lived, and the father and the little one died within a week of each other, and the sunshine of the young wife's life went down never to return—at least as far as earthly joys were concerned. There were those who were well skilled in reading the human countenance, who sometimes looked upon the old puckered face, and saw the smile that would light up the dim grey eyes when some little child 'drew near to gaze wistfully upon her apples and her oranges (always supposing of course that he or she only *gazed*) and who came to the conclusion that the heart that beat beneath the seemingly rough exterior was a very soft one, with a special place in it for all the weak and helpless things that GOD had made.

And all children, so long as they were honest, loved her very much, and would sit on her knee, at the hours when business was somewhat slack, and listen to the stories with which Apple Polly's head seemed so abundantly stored.

It was twelve o'clock one glaring July day; there were fewer people than usual in the crowded streets around Polly's corner; it seemed as though even the accustomed business of the great city must stop for a while beneath that glaring summer sun. The old woman herself nodded at intervals beneath her umbrella, and then when the numerous clocks sounded out the mid-day hour she gave herself an energetic shake and said, " Polly, this will never do, the folks will be coming out to their luncheon, and you must wake up," and then she took an old and very worn out Prayer Book from the depths of a very capacious blue pocket, which she always wore under her brown dress, and she began to read in a low voice the Collect, Epistle, and Gospel, for that week—the Seventh after Trinity. And then, as no customers came, Apple Polly soliloquised a bit as her fashion was, and the subject of her soliloquy was the sermon she had heard at Church the evening before.

" I minds what the Parson said : it was that we must ask GOD to graft in our hearts the love of His Name, and then if that Name was always before us, if we was ever a-thinking about it, and of Him Who bears it, why we should be kept from sin, and the wages of sin is death ; but the gift of GOD is Eternal Life, through JESUS CHRIST our LORD. Ah, yes, it's that that helps us through all our sorrows, and all our troubles, that hope of the great gift we shall all have, if we only tries to do what is right ; and Apple Polly lifted her old eyes to the cloudless blue sky, and a smile came upon the wrinkled features, as she thought of that great and infinite blessing which was bought for us by the

death of our own dear LORD,—even that gift o
Everlasting Life for which day by day in the
Creed, we confess that we look."

A minute or two passed away, and the smile
was exchanged for one of the old apple woman's
fiercest frowns, and the hushed voice for very
loud and angry tones, as Polly captured a little
hand which was in the act of stealing the larges
and ripest bunch of cherries, and drew the small
ragged form of the would-be thief, closer to he
knees.

"Now then, what do you mean, you little bad
wicked dirty child?"

It certainly was a very dirty little child whom
she addressed; a boy of some ten years old
with a great shock of yellow hair hanging a
over his smutty face, and two very small brigh
bead-like eyes shining out from beneath thos
tangled masses.

"I meant to take a bunch of cherries," wa
the unabashed, defiant answer.

"You did, did you?" answered Polly, givin
the offender a sound shaking, "then I tell yo
what I will do with you—I will give you up t
the next policeman as passes, and he will tak
you to prison, and lock you up."

"Oh, please don't, ma'am, please don't; i

deed I won't do it no more; but Tommie is *so* thirsty, and he axed me to get him a cooler— one of them cold things, you know, as they sells at the other corner of the street—but I hadn't ne'er a penny in the world, and I couldn't bag one, for 'twould have melted in my hand, and so I comed on here, and—and—"

"And took my cherries, you dirty wicked little boy, you."

"I knows I's dirty, I can't help that; there's no one to look after me nowheres. I belongs to nobody but Tommie, and he's too young."

Bad though the boy was, there was an honest truthful look in those twinkling eyes of his, and the tone in which he said, "there's no one to look after me nowheres, I belongs to nobody," had in it a strange unconscious pathos, which went straight to that soft spot which was kept green in Apple Polly's heart, by the ever-present memory of her little dead child."

"Who is Tommie?" she asked; "is he your brother?"

"No, I never had ne'er a one, nor father nor mother neither, as I knows on; he's a chap as I picked up one night on the wharf, and he've lived with me ever since, and I takes care of him. He's smaller than I am, ever so much smaller, and he's very weakly,—he's sick now, that's why I wanted the cherries."

"Poor little lad," and Polly, half ashamed of her weakness, drew the dirty boy more closely to her, and put back the yellow hair from the quaint brown face, "poor little lad, but you shouldn't have stole, my boy—you should have asked me to give you a bunch of cherries, and I'd have done it willingly."

"Would you, though? You see, I didn't know that; but next time I wants anything, I'll come and ask you for it, that I will."

"Will you take the cherries now?"

"No, thank you, I don't think I'd best take them; I don't think as how Tommie would like it if I told him that I had tried to steal, for he's a clever little chap, ma'am, and he's teaching me to be good, and telling me all about GOD, and about JESUS. I forgot it all when I seed the cherries, but I mustn't tell Tommie, for may be he'd cry, and that would make him worse."

"Where do you live, my man?"

"Down in the yard alongside of the river; we has a bed there in a room with six or seven other boys, and we pays for it regular, we do—for I earns a deal sometimes at the crossings, although to-day I is stumped up."

" Take the cherries home to Tommie, Jack."

" Jack !" echoed the urchin ; " well, that *is* a lark. Who ever told you to call me that ? why, my name is Pat,—everybody knows me as Pat."

" Well, Pat, take the cherries."

" No, I think I'd best not—leastways not now. Wait—Hullo, please, sir, you've dropped your handkercher," and Pat turned head' over heels, and picked up a pocket-handkerchief, which a gentleman had dropped out of his pocket, and presented it to him with his face all of a grin.

" Thanks, my boy," and a silver sixpence found its way into Pat's grimy palm.

In another minute, the boy had returned to Apple Polly's stall.

" Now, then, I'll have three bunches of cherries, and I'll come again to-morrow, and there'll be no need to tell Tommie how wicked I was."

" My dear," and the old withered hand was laid upon Pat's arm; " my dear, you should think that GOD is always looking down upon His children ; you should learn to love His Name, and then you wouldn't be tempted to do wrong things."

" That's what Tommie says : that's what I'm trying to learn. But oh, it's awful hard work ; for I've been a bad chap all my life, and when I

means to be good I forgets and forgets, and
goes all wrong again ;" and there were real tears
now in the dark eyes, and the dirty face had in
it a rueful, hopeless expression, which made
poor old Polly take up the corner of her apron
and turn away, so that Pat should not see that
she was trying to wipe away those tell-tale drops
which *would* roll down her old cheeks.

"I should like to come and see Tommie,"
she said.

Pat looked somewhat puzzled.

"Could you come in the mornings?" he
asked, "because if you couldn't, 'twould be no
good; the other chaps would only chaff you,
and tease Tommie."

"I don't well see how I could leave the
stall."

"I'd take care of it," was the bold reply.
"You could trust me, couldn't you?"

"Yes, I suppose I could; well, I'll try. Come
here at ten o'clock to-morrow, and then I'll go
off to the Yard, and leave you to mind the
business."

"Polly, you're an old fool," soliloquised the
apple woman, when her strange little friend had
turned away; "but never mind, it's better to
trust too much, than too little, and the lad had

that in his face which made me take to him wonderful."

Let us follow Pat to his miserable home—such a place as it was; down ever so many steps, into a dark cellar—dark even when the midday sun was shining over the great city in its glory and its strength. There were two or three heaps of straw upon the stone floor, and from one of these there came the sound of a little sickly voice.

" Pat, oh Pat, I thought you was never coming home."

" Tommie, look here," and the boy knelt by the side of that wretched bed, and held up the bunches of bright cherries before the little sick boy who lay there.

" Oh, Pat, where did you get them ?"

The thin eager face was lit up with a strange fearful expression, the blue eyes were fixed upon Pat's face, as though Tommie dreaded to hear the answer to the question he had asked.

Pat turned away as he said, " I did not steal them; I picked up a gentleman's pockethand-kercher, and he gave me sixpence; see here's the other threepence."

Then the little thin wasted arm was thrown

round the elder boy's neck, and Tommie drew the brown face down quite close to his and murmured,

"Oh, I'm so glad; I know 'twas wrong of me to be afeard, Pat, but I was a-reading in mother's Prayer Book about the Gift of God; and that's eternal life, which means heaven, and Pat, dear Pat, them as steals cannot go to live with JESUS above the bright blue sky."

"Tommie," answered the other, "'twas about that that the old woman at the fruit stall was reading when—when—when I stood by her a-looking at the cherries, and she's coming to see you to-morrow, Tommie, when the others is gone out, and I'm going to mind the stall, and I won't steal, indeed, indeed I won't, for I wants to go where the angels are, Tommie,—I wants to go to JESUS."

Pat had told the truth when he said that he did not know whether he had ever had a father or mother; his first memories dated back to a life more wretched than anything he had to undergo now, when he lived with a woman who used to send two or three little creatures like himself into the streets to beg, and who used to beat them mercilessly when they came home at night. One night she was not at her post, and she never came again, and from that time Pat went, as he was wont to express it, "on his own hook." How he had lived was best known to himself; I don't think he could ever have made any one quite understand what his poor little desolate life had been, how utterly friendless and miserable and uncared for.

One night he was wandering along the wharf, looking out for a night's lodging, it did not much matter where,—in an empty cart, or under an old piece of sacking,—and he met a little boy crying as though his heart would break.

He stopped him and asked what he was howling about; but though the words sounded rough and uncouth, there was a kindly light in the black eyes, and Tommie poured forth his tale into the sympathising ear of his new friend.

"Mother's dead,—they carried her away to the hospital yesterday, because she was so bad, —and I went there just now, and the gentleman told me she died this morning, and she was all I had, and now I'm quite alone."

"No, you ain't," was the prompt reply, "I'll take you and care for you, just like Ben Jones took the puppy as he picked up out of the water."

Poor Tommie, it was not a flattering comparison, but the poor little heart was yearning for love of some kind, and when Pat took his hand and led him on gently, he began to dry his tears, and to ask his new friend where he lived.

" Nowheres, but now I've took you, I'll find a place, and we'll live quite respectable, and I'll work, and when I can't get no work, I'll prig."

" No, no, you must not do that; GOD will not love you if you do, He will not take you to Heaven when you die."

It was the first time that Pat had ever heard either of GOD or of Heaven, but afterwards Tommie used to tell him all that his own dear mother who had died in the hospital had taught him, and Pat, who was sharp enough, soon learned all that his little teacher knew, and tried to mend his evil ways.

He was true to his word; he tried to get some work, and he took Tommie to that dark cellar the very next day, (the first night the two slept in an empty cart on the wharf,) and he never thought of himself, never seemed to care whether he had anything to eat or drink, so long as his little friend did not starve.

Tommie tried to work too, but when the

winter came the child's strength failed, and all through the bright spring-tide he lay upon the straw in the cellar; and Pat used to say, " When the summer comes, Tommie, you will be quite well."

" Yes, when the summer comes," Tommie would repeat, "we'll go out together then, and see the flowers in the Temple Gardens."

And now it *was* summer, and the little sick boy grew paler and thinner every day, and even the rough lads who used to come home at night to sleep in the cellar, hushed their swearing sometimes, and talked in low whispers, because of the little chap who they said to each other was dying.

Sometimes he would try and tell them of GOD and the Angels, and of the great gift which JESUS had given them,—the gift of Heaven.

But most of them laughed at him, and none of them heeded him, and the boy's life was passing quickly away in the lone dark cellar.

Pat kept his appointment punctually. Ten o'clock was striking as he stood before Apple Polly, his poor dirty face all smeared with the marks of tears.

" Oh, ma'am, please go and speak to Tommie,

I told him that I had heard you reading about the gift yesterday, the gift that JESUS came to bring us; and he wants to see you ever so badly, he wants you to help him to say his prayers, and to go to heaven; for he says he's much worse, and 'twon't be long before he dies."

So "Apple Polly" bustled off, and Pat sat upon her chair, under the old umbrella, and he would have felt very important, only he was too miserable to think of it; he had loved Tommie very much during those nine months that they had been together, and the thought of parting with him was very very bitter.

For those little ragged urchins whom we pass in the streets in our daily walks, have hearts, very loving tender hearts indeed some of them are blessed with; and remember it was for them as well as for us, that the Holy Sinless Child lived His childish life in His poor home at Nazareth; for them as well as for us, that He died that cruel death upon the Cross, so that He might win for them as for us, the Gift of Eternal Life.

Not once was poor Pat tempted to steal. "I must learn the way to Heaven," he kept on saying, "I must go to Tommie there."

He had very few customers, and the minutes

wore slowly on, and at last the old woman came back, flurried and excited.

"I've been a long way, Pat, right out to a doctor as I knows, and we must go and take Tommie to the hospital; he can't stay in that 'ere place, poor little man."

"He shan't leave me," cried Pat, bursting into a passionate flood of tears ; "he'll die sooner if they take him to the hospital; 'twas that as made his mother die."

Very gently Apple Polly reasoned with the poor little fellow. "They'll make him so comfortable there, Pat," she said, "and the doctor says you may go to see him every day; come with me now, I'm going to pack up; the folks will wonder where old Apple Polly's gone today, but GOD has put it into my heart to be kind to you two poor little orphan lads."

No sooner said than done—in a very few minutes the stall and its contents were deposited in Polly's room, which was situated very near her corner, and then she and Pat got into a cab, and they took Tommie from the wretched cellar, and drove him to a bright cheerful hospital, where he was laid upon a little white bed, looking as happy and contented as a young prince.

Every day the old woman and the little boy visited Tommie in his new home; he had rallied a little after the first, and oh, how he used to long for the sight of Pat's dirty face and yellow hair.

Once he had said to Polly, "When I'm gone will you tell him about the Gift JESUS gave us? will you teach him the way to heaven? I've asked the parson here to speak to him as he spoke to me; he's made it all so clear like, and taught me how to bear the pain, but Pat is a rum chap, he won't have nothing to say to the parson, he says he only likes you and me."

"My dear, I'll do my best," and Apple Polly rubbed her old eyes more violently than usual, as she stooped and kissed the poor little thin face.

The July moon in all its brightness shone into the hospital ward. All was still—all shut up for the night. Only by the side of Tommie's bed sat a Sister of Mercy reading to him about the beautiful country which is GOD's gift to us.

Suddenly he stopped her. "Sister," he said, "dear Sister, do you think Pat was ever baptised?"

The Sister started; strange to say no one had

thought of that before; they had all been watching Tommie, and Pat had not received much notice in that busy place.

"Sister, I wants him now; I wants to tell him to come to me, and if he has never been made God's own child, that will help him to be good now. Oh, send for him, please, for there's not much time, I cannot see your face plainly, Sister, and I wants to see his once more, because he's been so good to me ever since mother died."

Sister Clare did as Tommie wished; the child closed his eyes, and joined his little hands upon his breast, and the moonbeams fell upon his face, and lit it up with a glow that had nothing of earth about it, and when, half an hour afterwards, Pat stood and looked upon his little friend, he thought that God had made him more beautiful than he had ever been before, so that he might be fit to go to the Angels.

"Tommie, Tommie," he whispered, "please take me with you."

And Tommie opened his eyes, and fixed them upon that quaint face with a look of love unutterable.

"Pat, good-bye; Sister will tell you about it, Pat, and the HOLY GHOST will be with you al-

ways to show you the way; he said the verse
to-day, the parson did—the same as mother
used to tell me. The gift of GOD is Eternal
Life : through JESUS CHRIST our LORD. And
he gave me the Blessed Sacrament ; the Gift as
JESUS left us here, to bring us to Heaven at last.
And now, Pat, let me lie on your shoulder as I
used to do."

And Pat climbed upon the little bed, and
Tommie laid his head upon its old resting place;
and when the golden sun lit up the hospital ward
its rays fell upon two sleeping boys, and one
opened his dark eyes and looked around him
wonderingly, and the other lay all calm and still
and beautiful, in that sleep which is called death.

But the gift of GOD is Eternal Life, through
JESUS CHRIST our LORD.

A few weeks more and Pat stood at the Holy
Font, and received the strength which would
enable him to win the prize and the gift, for
which his LORD died.

Very silent and subdued was the once saucy
ragged urchin, as he looked into Apple Polly's
face as he left the Church and said, " 'Twill be
easier to find the way now, to where Tommie is."

And for answer the old woman caught hold
of the boy's hand and did not leave go of it,

until she had got him safely seated in a chair in her own room.

"Pat," she said, "I've got a deal of money."

"Yes," answered Pat, "I know you have; I seed a whole half-crown in your purse when you opened it."

"But, Pat, I've got some money in the bank, and I'm a-going to send you to school, and to learn how to sing in Church: you'll like that, won't you? I've spoken to the clergyman, and it's all right."

And poor Pat burst into tears and answered, "Oh, Tommie will see me, and he'll be so glad, and I'll try never to lose the gift—that JESUS has given me."

Apple Polly kept her word; she kept the boy in her own home, taking a little attic at the top of the house for him to sleep in, and that room seemed to Pat the most luxurious apartment possible after the wretched cellar in which those last months had been spent.

Sometimes he longed for Tommie, but he knew the wish was a selfish one; he was learning to realize what that happiness must be to which his little friend had gone, learning to purify himself that he might go to where Tommie was.

He knew now how bad he had been; he could see by the help of the HOLY SPIRIT which had been given him in his baptism, how grievous in the sight of GOD must be the many sins which he had committed, but he knew too there was pardon and peace to be found even on earth; the honest truthful nature kept back nothing of the past, did not seek to palliate or gloss over one sin of those by-gone years, the discipline was very sharp, the penitence very real; temptations crowded on Pat still; do they not crowd upon us all? but they were bravely resisted and struggled against, and GOD's own Priest told the boy in the Name of the FATHER, and of the SON, and of the HOLY GHOST, that he was cleansed from the load of guilt by the precious Blood of JESUS.

Thorough in all things was our young hero; and after all his sorrow a great new joy came into his life.

"Polly," he said, one winter's day, his honest face all of a glow, "Polly, the Bishop is coming, and I am to be confirmed; and after that," and the eager voice was hushed into low reverent tones, "after that, in the Blessed Sacrament, I shall be nearer Tommie than I have ever been before."

Last time I saw Apple Polly was in Church,
at an early Celebration, and it seemed to me as
though the old face had got younger in those
three years that had elapsed since last I gazed
upon it. Only the tears rolled down the old
cheeks as a yellow-haired chorister knelt at the
Altar, and received the heavenly food which
should preserve his body and soul unto Everlasting Life.

"I go to life, and not to death,
From darkness to life's native sky;
I go from sickness and from pain
To health and immortality.
   Let our farewell then be tearless,
   Since I bid farewell to tears;
   Write this day of my departure
   Festive in your coming years.

"I go from poverty to wealth,
From rags to raiment angel-fair,
From the pale leanness of this flesh,
To beauty such as Saints shall wear.
   Let our farewell, &c.

"I go from chains to liberty;
These fetters will be broken soon.
Forth over Eden's fragrant fields
I walk beneath a glorious noon.
   Let our farewell, &c.

"For toil there comes the crownèd rest,
Instead of burdens eagles' wings ;
And I, even I, this life-long thirst
Shall quench at everlasting springs.
    Let our farewell, &c.

"GOD lives ! Who says that I must die ?
I cannot, while JEHOVAH liveth.
CHRIST lives ! I cannot die, but live,
He life to me for ever giveth.
    Let our farewell, &c."

HURTFUL THINGS.

Eighth Sunday after Trinity.

> "That He in all we do or say,
> Would keep us free from harm to-day."

"IF you please, ma'am, what are hurtful things?"

I was taking my usual Sunday afternoon class at S. Agnes', a crowded, densely-populated parish in the north-east of London, and the above question was asked me by a heavy, stunted, stolid-looking girl, Anne Forbes by name, who had hardly ever, so far as I could remember, addressed one single voluntary remark to me during the whole twelve months of our acquaintance.

There was a general titter amongst the other girls at the sound of the low sweet voice, for in spite of the plain face, and crooked figure, and

V.   E

uncouth awkward manner, Anne Forbes' voice
was very low and sweet, strangely at variance
with the loud, rough tones of most of her companions.

I had tried to talk to her sometimes, but had
always failed to make anything of her, or in any
way to interest her. I really was not quite sure
that she heard or understood half I said; for
there she used to sit during all that long hour
on Sunday afternoons, and not the smallest ray
of intelligence ever seemed to me to light up
the stolid unimpressionable face, which looked
up at me with the same dreary expression upon
it, through the whole time of teaching.

I could not even find out where Anne lived;
the first time I asked for her address, she answered, "It don't matter, thank you, we are
going to move next week." I went away for a
month after that Sunday, and when I next
sought for information respecting poor Anne's
habitation, I received the same answer, to the
very evident amusement of the other girls.

She had no father, I gleaned, only a mother,
and something of a very faint blush came to the
sallow cheek when I inquired on one occasion
why she had been absent on the previous Sunday, and she said, "Mother wanted me."

"Was she ill?" I asked, really hoping to induce the girl to speak to me.

"No, she was not ill;" and I saw that Anne did not mean to say another word upon the subject.

So the weeks and months passed on, and I knew no more of my poor scholar than I had done when first she came, and because she was fifteen or sixteen years of age, she had been put with the other elder girls into my class, and the superintendent asked me with a hopeless smile upon her face to do what I could with her.

They were for the most part a rough ignorant set, those poor girls with whom I had to deal week after week. Their lives were spent amidst scenes of no ordinary temptation; some of them had only recently been baptised, none of them were as yet confirmed, but about a fortnight before that Sunday of which I am writing, the Rector gave out that a Confirmation would be held before Christmas, and most of my children, and amongst the number Anne Forbes, had sent in their names as candidates for the holy Sacramental Rite.

I had been talking to them only for a few minutes on that July afternoon, telling them how they must pray that they might be kept

from harm, and be faithful to their Baptisma
Vows; and whilst I was in the middle of a sen
tence came Anne Forbes' question, "If yo
please, ma'am, what are hurtful things?"

Truth to tell I was rather puzzled what t
reply. I knew that the girl did not mean m
to speak in very general terms, and that some
thing particular was on her mind, so I did th
best I could, and said,

"It is rather a hard question to answe
Anne; you all of you know that there are som
things which must harm us all, such as goin
into bad company, or listening to, and joinin
in, bad language; but as we go through th
world we must ask GOD to keep us from speci
temptations,—I mean by this from things tha
hurt ourselves specially. I will give you an i
stance of what I want you to understand,—on
of you may be very fond of dress, and long fo
a piece of bright ribbon or something of tha
kind, and at last may spend the money on
that you ought to have taken home to you
mothers on Saturday nights; whilst anothe
may buy the piece of ribbon, and be quite righ
in doing so, and what is a hurtful thing to on
is an innocent thing to the other. And so it
in whatever we do,—what is right for other

may be wrong for us, what is a temptation to one of you may be no temptation at all to another,—GOD only knows the secrets of our hearts; He has given us all, His HOLY SPIRIT to help us to choose between right and wrong, and in great things as well as in small things we must ask Him to show us what is hurtful, and also what is profitable for our salvation,—that is, for the good of our souls.

"I have begun with one small instance of a hurtful thing, I will give you another and a greater one. I think that perhaps the love of being first, the temptation of outdoing those around us, is one of the greatest snares that come into our way,—and therefore anything that fosters our vanity is a hurtful thing,—and yet even here there are exceptions to the rule; there are some who think so humbly of themselves, who are so timid and shrinking and gentle, that they always put themselves last, instead of first, and who seem to be sent into the world to bear the burdens that others lay upon them; praise and notice to them are not hurtful things, they are little helps that GOD sends them on their onward way, glimpses, as it were, of a far-away brightness of which they have never dreamed, of a day when life's weary journey

shall be over, and when they will bask for ever
and for ever in the sunshine of GOD's Love.

"My dear girls, I know how many difficulties,
and how many temptations come into your daily
lives,—how those who only see the surface, that
is, the outside of things, would say that hurtful
things are always around you; how the very air
you breathe is full of them. And yet although
it is so, you can keep them away from yourselves, or rather you can ask GOD to keep them
away from you. You can be quite pure and
good and true if you will only remember that
the Holy JESUS Who died for you is ever near
you to help you to be meek and gentle as He
was. I know that this sounds hard to you; I
know you will tell me that it is very difficult for
you to do all that you ought to do; sometimes
even to say your prayers, and to go to Church,
involves some trouble, it may be some suffering.

"You have worked hard all day, and you are
tired when night comes, and perhaps there are
others in the room, and you think you can say
your prayers when you get into bed; and then
sleep comes almost before you know it, and no
prayers at all are said. In the morning too the
weariness is upon you; you jump up at the last
minute and go to your work, and you do not

kneel down and ask God to keep all hurtful things away from you during the day. You go out like soldiers to the battle, but you don't take your weapons with you, and the enemy comes, that enemy the devil, of whom I have so often spoken to you, and you have no power to resist temptation, and like foolish soldiers who leave their guns at home, and so fall beneath the fire of the foe, you allow hurtful things to come near you, whilst had you prayed that they might be put away from you, you would have conquered in the fight.

"I am afraid even now I have hardly made you understand all I mean. It is just this : You cannot choose where you are to live, nor the people amongst whom your life is to be spent. God orders all things for you; of course you must not willingly put yourselves into what you know would be an occasion of sin, but so long as you are doing your duty honestly where you are placed, and trying with all your heart to please your Master, Jesus Christ, the things that look hurtful to others will not be allowed to hurt you ; the very battle against sin will purify you, and make you stronger and better, and more fit for the Kingdom of Heaven.

"Dear children, in to-day's Epistle we read

that we are 'heirs of GOD, and joint heirs with CHRIST ; if so be that we suffer with Him, that we may be also glorified together.'

"Surely the thought of this ought to make us patient. What need we care for the troubles that come into our lives, with that hope, ay, that certainty at the end, that if we suffer with Him, patiently, uncomplainingly, even as He suffered for us, we shall be glorified with Him, live with Him for ever in the Beautiful, Heavenly Jerusalem."

The Church bell was ringing before I had finished speaking to my girls, and when I looked up to tell them that it was time to disperse, I saw Anne Forbes' eyes fixed upon me with an expression in them that I had never seen there before. There was a flush upon the sallow cheeks, a light in the dull dark eyes, and the poor thin hands were clasped nervously, and the girl's lips were parted as if she were anxious to speak ; but there was no time for a word, every one had to hurry off as fast as possible, and only once I caught sight of poor Anne, as she knelt in her usual corner in Church behind all the others. There was no appointed place for my class ; the girls were supposed to come voluntarily, and I always noticed that Anne got quite out of the way, as though she would avoid notice.

The girl's face was eager still, as I saw her kneeling there, but I thought I saw tears rolling down her cheeks, and I determined if possible to try and help her in her trouble whatever it was, more than I had ever done before.

I saw all my other children out of Church, and I waited a long time for Anne ; she did not appear, and I looked into the Sacred Building and saw her kneeling where I had left her, her head bowed upon her hands, her whole form quivering with emotion. I could not bear to leave her thus, and yet I did not like to disturb her, I felt that the poor child was praying that hurtful things might be kept away from her, and I wondered what hard, stern duties those were that came into her life, and my heart yearned to her in her evident trouble, more than to any of those brighter, more cheery maidens, with whom I had just parted.

I knelt in the Church also, and asked GOD to help *me*, to help my poor scholar.

Anne rose from her knees at last, and when she saw me, she started and tried to get out of the door, so as not to be obliged to speak to me.

I followed her, and laid my hand upon her shoulder; "My child," I said, "you are unhappy, may I know the reason?"

"No, no, please let me go, I'm late already, and she'll be so angry, oh please let me go."

"I will not keep you against your wish; but, dear child, if I could only help you, if I could save you from coming into contact with hurtful things."

I had touched the right chord then,—the barrier that had kept us apart from each other for all those months was broken down, as we stood together in the crowded street on that bright July afternoon, the sunshine streaming down upon our heads, and making even that dingy London thoroughfare seem more than usually cheerful.

"Oh, ma'am, it's that I wants; I do try so hard, but I'm always failing, always going wrong; and I do so want to learn to be good, and to go to the Beautiful City, but you can't help me, indeed you can't, unless—" and poor Anne hung her head awkwardly, and spoke in a low whisper —"unless perhaps you would say a prayer, and ask GOD to make me a good girl."

"Will you let me go home with you?" I asked.

"No, no, you mustn't, it isn't fit for you to come there."

"I am not afraid," I answered, smiling, "I have been to most places in London, I do not think you can show me anything worse than I have already seen."

"But it would only make it harder for me, if you was to come."

The argument was an incontrovertible one, I would not willingly have laid one more trouble upon that poor weary child's heart.

"I will take you part of the way," I said, and I made Anne take my arm; she looked so ill, and so tired; and she walked shyly by my side, and truth to tell I did not know what to say by way of comfort or of help.

"Is your mother better?" I asked at last; never having heard that she was ill, the question was, to say the least of it, a hazardous one.

"She ain't bad," was the answer, "at least she wasn't a week agone, she have not been home since."

"And with whom do you live?"

"I lives alone when she goes away."

"And what do you do?"

"Sack-making,—I earns enough to live upon, and enough for mother too when she's there."

So this was the story of that poor young life,
—a life spent in loneliness, wearing itself out
for another.

"Anne, my dear," I said, "why are you so
frightened? why will you not let me be your
friend?"

In spite of herself, and of her evident determination not to complain, the words came out,

"I can't tell you all I have to bear; it wouldn't
be right or fair."

I would not press her any further then; and
she stopped at the corner of a dirty yard, and
said,

"It is here we live, you must not come on."

"You are alone, my child, may I not go in
with you?"

"No, don't ask it, ma'am, indeed, indeed you
mustn't."

"Then good-bye, dear child, I shall see you
next Sunday, I hope, and in the mean time remember, that no hurtful things—I mean things
that look hurtful to others—can really harm you,
if you pray to GOD to keep you safe, and try to
remember that He is always near you, to watch
over you and to help you. And one word more,
Anne, 'if we suffer with Him, we shall be glorified with Him.'"

Again that look of mingled hope and joy came upon the girl's face, and then she left me; but I felt very happy, and very thankful on that afternoon, for it seemed as though GOD in His infinite mercy had allowed me to send one small ray of comfort into the heart of that child of His, Who in her own poor way was trying so hard to be good.

I stood there watching the stunted figure, as Anne walked slowly through the dirty yard; sounds of blasphemy, and swearing, and obscene merriment fell upon my ear, and I trembled when I thought of the scenes in which the lives of most of my Sunday class were spent, and of the hurtful things which only He Who loved them well enough to die for them, could put away from them, if they asked Him in His never-failing Providence to be their Guide, and their Friend.

Strange to say, at that moment I thought more of the others than of Anne; I had less fear for her, the poor stupid stolid-looking girl, whom the rest of them seemed more or less inclined to despise, but who was so fearful for herself, than I had for some of the bright clever maidens who were never at a loss for an answer when I questioned them as to their duties and responsibilities as members of CHRIST, children of GOD, and inheritors of the Kingdom of Heaven.

I thought very much of poor Anne during the week that followed that Eighth Sunday after Trinity of which I have been telling you ; the echoes of those loud voices which had come from the dirty yard were still it seemed ringing in my ears, those words of blasphemy which I had heard still made me shudder whenever they came to mind ; would these hurtful things really harm poor Anne, or would she escape unscathed, shielded by faith, armed by prayer ?

The poor girl was not in her place when the next Sunday came. I confess to watching for her anxiously, and to hoping almost to the last moment that she would appear, for she had sometimes come in late, looking shy and flustered.

I watched and hoped in vain, and I turned to Kate Robinson, who I knew lived somewhere in the neighbourhood of Geranium Yard, and asked her if she knew anything of Anne Forbes.

I saw her glance at the others and smile, and then look doubtfully at me ; I had always discouraged anything like gossip amongst the girls in my presence, but I knew now that there was something to tell, and that Kate was doubtful as to the propriety of relating the fact whatever it might be.

My curiosity got the better of my usual discretion, and I said,

"What is it, Kate? is anything the matter? you need not be afraid of telling me what you know."

"Please, ma'am, haven't you heard? it's in the paper."

"No, I have heard nothing; what do you mean, child?" I am afraid I spoke sharply, for a strange foreboding of evil was at my heart.

"Please, ma'am, Anne's mother have been took up, and put into prison; there was a lot of things found in the house that she had stole, and the perlice took her right away. And they took Anne too, but they've let *her* go again, because she knowed nothing about it."

"Where is she now?" I asked, anxiously.

"Nobody knows, ma'am; she went right away, and nobody have seen her since Wednesday night."

"She was in Church then," said another, "I seed her coming out, but she wouldn't so much

as look at me; she held her head down, and
runned along, as if she was afeard that I'd bite
her."

"Poor child," I said; "and is that all you
know?"

"No, ma'am, there's more to tell. Anne's
mother went before the judge on Thursday,
and she've got five years in prison, with hard
labour."

That was all : not another word of my poor
scholar, not one clue to her whereabouts. I
could but go into the Church and pray for her,
as I had done all through the week that had
passed away, that GOD in His mercy would put
away from her all hurtful things, and that amidst
the trials and sufferings that I knew must come
into her life, she would find peace in the thought
of the never ceasing Love and care of Him Who
died for her. A few days afterwards I sought
and obtained permission to visit Anne's mother
in prison.

I found a sullen, dogged-looking woman, who
at first refused to speak to me, but when I said
something about Anne, just the faintest light of
tenderness came into her dark eyes, and she
told me that she did not know where the girl
had gone.

" She spoke a word to me when the sentence was passed, and she asked me to kiss her, and then the poor thing walked away crying bitterly."

There seemed no feeling of penitence in the woman's heart for all the wrong she had done. I gleaned that she belonged to a gang of thieves, who had long been under the eye of the police, and that this was not the first time that she had been in prison. And to my joy, I found out that the child, although she knew all about the terrible life her mother led, had never been induced to join in any of her wicked practices.

" Her father was a soldier," the woman said, " as honest a fellow as ever lived, and I suppose Anne took after him, for I've beat her many and many a time to try and make her do things, and she wouldn't as much as touch a bit of food that comed into the house, if she thought it had not been got honestly."

This was all I heard, but it made me very thankful ; and I felt that wherever Anne might be, hurtful things would be put away from her, because of the true, honest purpose of the poor girl's heart.

The Confirmation day came ; most of the

girls in my class were confirmed, and I trusted and hoped and prayed that the sevenfold gifts of grace might be theirs for evermore.

Very soon afterwards circumstances obliged me to leave London. I heard of my scholars at intervals both from themselves and from others, and at some of the tales told in those letters I rejoiced, whilst others made me very sad—for some were doing their duty honestly, and leading honest, GOD fearing lives, going regularly to Church and Holy Communion, whilst others— but I will not tell of the others here; and GOD is very merciful, and even yet I hope that the bread cast upon the waters may be found, although it may be after many days.

Five years had passed away since that Sunday when I had spoken to my children about hurtful things, and now I was far away from the scene of my old labours. I had given my life to GOD in His Church as a Sister of Mercy. I was one of a small community who were working amongst the poor, and the sick, and the needy, in a large manufacturing town.

We always had plenty to do, but during that summer of which I am now writing our hands were unusually full, for fever of the most malignant kind had broken out in the crowded streets and lanes and courts of Mannerton, and from morning till night we were with those poor sick and dying creatures, speaking to them of hope beyond the grave, of life for evermore for JESUS' sake.

One July evening—a Sunday evening it was— I was sent to a court down by the river, where I was told there were five or six people in one house laid low by the terrible scourge that GOD had sent us.

" Is no one taking care of the poor things ?" I asked of the girl who was waiting to be my guide to Blue Anchor Court.

" No, Sister, no one, unless it's Anne, and she can't be in every place at once. She've been up these four nights, and she's most tired out, I'm thinking ; she looked terrible bad when I came away to fetch you, and says she, ' Ask one of the good Sisters to come, and try to save some of them, body and soul ;' and then she put her hand to her head, and she most fainted on the doorstep."

" Who is Anne ?" I inquired.

" Why, she's crooked Anne, as works at the factory, and lives along of old Mother White. You must have seen her at Church, Sister, she's always there, Sundays and week-a-days, and she tries to teach us to be good, she do, and I loves her dearly." And my companion's honest good-natured face beamed with affection and gratitude.

"Here we is, Sister; there's two sick in the first floor back, and two in the second floor front, and three in the top garret."

I went in to see them all—men, women, and children, all more or less ill, some lying there in their death agony. I sent for one of the Priests to come to the infected house, and words of pardon and of peace fell upon weary ears, when weak faltering tongues had told their tale of sin, and asked for GOD's mercy.

I was standing closing the eyes of a little child who had gone to her rest, when Madge, the girl who had come to the Home to summon me to Blue Anchor Court, entered the room, looking aghast and terrified. She laid her hand upon mine entreatingly.

"Oh, Sister, please come, she's very bad now; she've got it, I'm quite sure."

I followed her up to the back attic, and there upon the low bed, her face flushed with fever, lay my old scholar, Anne Forbes.

I bent over her, lovingly and thankfully. I

had always hoped and prayed that we might meet again.

The dark eyes looked wistfully into mine; and then the hands were clasped as though in prayer, and a faint smile of recognition showed me that, in spite of my Sister's dress, Anne knew me.

" Oh, ma'am—oh, Sister, I went to Church this morning, and to the Blessed Sacrament, and that will keep us, won't it, from all hurtful things ?"

I saw that the sight of my face had brought back a whole flood of recollections to the poor girl's mind, and I stooped and kissed the burning brow, and said,

" Yes, my child, safe for ever; until we go to our own true Home, and no harm can ever come to us, for we shall be safe for ever with JESUS."

She closed her eyes then, but after a time she opened them again, and said, " Mother was so sorry."

I did not understand the allusion, and turned to Madge for information.

" She went to London about a month agone to see her mother; she was going to bring her back here, but she died."

I knew then that Anne's mother had been repentant at the last, and I prayed to GOD in that dreary attic for the dead parent and for the living child.

Anne was very ill for many days, and then the doctor said that there was hope that she might recover. She was moved to the Home before long, and soon she was able to tell me the story of those five years.

She and her mother had lived in Mannerton in the old days, and when that terrible blow came to her, she had determined to seek out old Widow White, and ask her to give her a home.

She had her week's wages in her pocket, and she made her way to Mannerton, and there she had lived ever since, until a month before, when she had gone to London to bring her mother home. She found her in the Infirmary, a penitent, dying woman, and the child came back to her lonely life once more.

"I was confirmed, Sister," she said, "four years agone, and I tried to do what was right; and GOD has been very good, and kept the hurtful things away, and if I go on and bear things, perhaps some day happiness will come to me. I mean that happiness as you told us about that Sunday ever so long ago."

Anne lives at the Home, and I think even now a foretaste of the happiness for which she so longs has come into the girl's life. She is always loving, and gentle and true, and sometimes as I walk along the streets, I see her talking kindly to some poor ragged girl,—speaking to her of the hope that came to her on that July Sunday all those years ago.

But it is in Church I like best to see her; it is there that the real true joy comes to my poor girl—for when she kneels in the Most Sacred Presence, and feeds upon the Life-giving food, she feels that she is indeed GOD's own child, an heir of the Heavenly FATHER, a joint heir of the Holy SON ; and if we suffer with Him here, we shall through His Infinite Mercy be glorified with Him, through all the great hereafter.

Into the lives of all of us, as into the life of this poor girl, hurtful things will, ay, must come; but thanks be to GOD, His never failing Providence orders all things for us, and if we pray to Him with all our hearts, He will in His great mercy put away from us all that can harm our souls, and give us all those things which are profitable for our salvation, because of His Love Who for our sakes endured temptation, so that He might be able to succour those that are tempted.

Be Thou my soul's preserver,
For Thou alone dost know
How many are the perils
Through which I have to go ;
O loving JESU, hear my call,
And guard and save me from them all.

HONEST BEN.

Ninth Sunday after Trinity.

"Let him that thinketh he standeth, take heed lest he fall."

A HUSBAND and wife and two little children were sitting at tea in a neat tidy cottage in the picturesque village of Charleton one sweet July evening not very long ago.

The birds were singing their sweetest songs, their lullaby to the fast closing day; the little insects were buzzing in the bright soft air, the woodbine and clematis which covered the little low porch sent their sweet fragrance through the open window into the trim parlour; there was nothing to disturb the inmates of that little room, not a sound of the weary work-a-day world

was to be heard, nothing but the merry chatter
of the children as they ate their bread and
treacle with evident relish, and talked of the
flowers in their little gardens, which were growing so fast in the bright summer sunshine.

John Mason and his wife looked at their
darlings lovingly : they were two tiny boys, of
the respective ages of four and five years : in
the churchyard on the hill-side were three little
graves, where three little ones who had been
taken into their LORD's own keeping had been
laid to their rest, and then as gifts from GOD
had come those boys, who were the joy and
sunshine of the Masons' cottage.

There were two fine lads of thirteen and fourteen years old, who held an equal place with
their little brothers in their parents' heart, and
for whom they were waiting now as they lin-
gered over their tea and listened to Willie's and
Neddie's baby talk.

" They are late," said the mother, looking
just a little anxious, " and they really ought to
have made haste, for to-night is practice-night,
and they'll not get any tea; there's the first bell
for Church now."

" That's their own look-out, Betsy," answered
John Mason cheerily, " it won't do them any

harm to go without a meal for once, and it will teach them to be more punctual for the future."

His wife sighed and smiled at the same time.

" I know Roger is safe," she said, " but somehow I'm always afraid for Ben."

There was an expression upon John Mason's honest face that was half grave, half comical, as he answered,

"Sometimes trust is misplaced, Betsy, and those as we fears for most, really gives us the least cause for fear in the end, whilst those as we trusts most sometimes turns out just the contrary way; I ain't saying that it will be so with our boys, Betsy, only—"

" Here's Roger," shouted the two small boys in chorus, and down they jumped from their high chairs to greet their elder brother, and hold up their little sticky mouths for the usual fraternal kiss.

Roger, however, looked very grave, and put the two little fellows from him gently, and then he stood looking first at his father and then at his mother, evidently wanting to speak, and yet not knowing what to say.

"Roger, what is it?" said Mrs. Mason, anxiously and hurriedly.

But still Roger did not speak, and his eyes were fixed upon the long straight road which lay in front of the cottage window, as though he were watching for some one to appear in the distance, and help him out of his difficulty.

"Roger, speak out, is anything the matter with you?"

"Not with *me*," and there was just the faintest touch of complacency in the boy's tone, difficult and almost impossible to detect through the real sorrow that was in his voice, as he answered, "not with me, father, but—but with Ben."

"What is it? oh, Roger, say, he is not hurt?" and the mother's hand was laid entreatingly upon her firstborn's arm.

"No, no, he is all right, safe, and well, he will be here directly, but—"

"But what? out with it, Roger, don't keep us in suspense longer than you can help."

"But he has been sent out of the choir; he is not to be a chorister any more."

"Why, what has he done?"

"I had rather not tell you, here he comes, he will speak for himself."

A boy opened the door quickly; a fine looking young fellow was Ben Mason, "not quite as handsome" as his brother Roger, folks said, and yet with an open honest look upon his face that won all hearts.

He certainly was not looking his best now; his cheeks were very red, and his hair very rough, and there was a frown upon his brow, and a general look of ill-temper upon his usually merry features which all told a tale of some special vexation or excitement.

And yet the blue eyes were raised fearlessly to his father's face; whatever had so ruffled the lad, and there was no doubt that he was very much ruffled, had not taken away the truthful, fearless look which ever since he had been a baby had won for him the name of " Honest Ben."

John Mason was as good a fellow as ever breathed; a most loving husband, a most tender father, but he had one great fault—a quick, hasty temper, which sometimes prevented him from looking at things as calmly, or judging as dispassionately as his usual good sense ought to have allowed him to do.

Now Roger's words were ringing in his ears, to the exclusion of all reason : " Ben has been sent out of the choir, he is not to be a chorister anv more."

John himself had been in the choir ever since he was a boy, and the idea of one of his sons being turned out of it, was more than he could stand.

"So you have brought disgrace upon us all, sir," he said, looking sternly at poor Ben; "I always said you would, with those wild, heedless ways of yours."

John, like a great many other people, forgot in the heat of passion that he had expressed an exactly contrary opinion five minutes before, and had insinuated to his wife that it was just possible that steady, sedate Roger, might give his parents more trouble than giddy, heedless Ben.

"Yes, sir, you have disgraced us," he repeated in a still louder tone, and Willie and Neddie retired into a distant corner and began to cry; for to do John Mason justice, it was very seldom that his children heard his voice raised in such a way as it was on that sweet, calm, peaceful July evening.

And through it all Ben stood there, the angry flush gone from his face, and a strange unusual look of determination in his blue eyes.

"Speak, sir, and tell us the reason of this trouble that has come upon us through you."

Ben looked imploringly at his brother; Roger turned his head away.

" Have you not told them, Roger ?"

" No, he has told us nothing but the fact, that was enough for him to do, he has left the rest to you."

With a great effort Ben spoke.

" I am turned out of the choir,—that *is* true, —but it is not true that I have done that of which I am accused."

A smile was on the mother's face then ; she had always really trusted her younger son ; the one bugbear of her life was lest his climbing propensities should get him into mischief,—of any moral fall, she had no fear.

" My own brave boy," she said, as she went up and kissed Ben's pale cheek. " I knew you would be able to explain all, and that every-thing would be right."

The first tear that Ben had shed during all that painful scene was in his eye then, and was hastily dashed away as he turned and looked at the mother he loved so dearly.

" But mother, dear, I cannot explain it ; I must bear the punishment," and then the poor fellow could endure the agony no longer, and he rushed out of the cottage door, and they saw him running across the road into the woods, there to hide his misery, and cry his poor little tender heart out, whilst the birds sang their evening song, and the sun sank to his rest behind the noble trees.

Roger would have followed his brother, but his father stopped him.

"Tell us at once," he said, "without any further nonsense, what all this means."

And so upon Roger it devolved to tell the tale, which was to cast such a heavy burden upon his father's and mother's heart.

It was told with many interruptions, and it will be better for us to go back a little in our story and see what had happened at the village school on that July afternoon. We must first say a little more about the brothers.

Roger Mason was training for a pupil teacher; he did not much like his work, but he was a clever, studious, intelligent lad, and his father had wished him to try to be a schoolmaster.

"If you don't like it by-and-by you need not do it, my boy," he had said, "but a little more learning whilst you are young won't do you any harm."

And honest Ben was at the head of the first class; clever and intelligent too, but certainly not studious; the leader of all fun, sometimes it must be confessed the promoter of a little bit of mischief. He was often in a scrape, there was many a big black mark to be found against the boy's name in the school register; he was so fond of play, so delighted in climbing trees and jumping what seemed to others impossible heights, that often the school bell had stopped long before he appeared, and when he was rebuked he would look up honestly and say, " I am very sorry, sir, but I felt as if I must have a good climb and a jump this morning."

Somehow every one loved Ben; every one went to him with their troubles, and when he had to help others he became grave and steady as an old judge, and the merry face was often clouded by the sorrows of those around him.

There was a boy in the village, by name Arthur Willis, who was Ben's especial friend. He was not a nice boy; John Mason and his wife did not consider him a very good companion for their son; and Roger would have nothing to say to him. Ben, who was generally very obedient, was somewhat obstinate upon the point of this friendship.

" Of course, father, if you say I ain't to have nothing to do with him, I mustn't; but please don't, for indeed he ain't a bad fellow, and he's so poor, and his mother is so ill, and he loves her so much."

And John Mason couldn't find it in his kind heart to take the one pleasure out of Arthur Willis' life.

"He don't do Ben any harm," he said to his wife, "the lad is too true and honest to be done harm to by any one, but somehow I don't like Willis, and I wish things was different."

It was quite a puzzle to every one what there was in the boy to attract Ben towards him. He was a surly, sulky young fellow, with an expression upon his face that was anything but pleasant, and when he spoke it was generally to grumble or to find fault with his companions. His mother was a widow; he was her only child. It was his one redeeming point, that love for the poor ailing woman, of which Ben had spoken; to her he was generally tender and gentle, and the poor thing lying almost always upon her hard bed thought that there was not a better lad in all Charleton than her Arthur.

In his way young Willis cared for Ben; he was as grateful as it was in his nature to be for the many acts of kindness the other had shown him, and he would not willingly have done him any harm ; on the contrary he would have done him a good turn, had it been at no cost to himself.

He had left school more than two years, and went to work at some little distance, and so he and Ben saw very little of each other now. They had met the evening before our story begins. Ben was on his way to Church, and Arthur was hurrying home from his work.

"What, off to Church again, Ben? catch me going every time the bells ring."

"I know you can't come on week days, Arthur, but I do wish you would try and come on Sundays ; indeed you don't know how it would help you ; you could pray to God to make your mother well there, ever so much better than you can at home, because you know that it is His own House, where He especially dwells," and Ben lowered his voice, and the colour rushed to his cheeks, as it always did when he spoke of holy things, and all the time he was speaking he was clasping and unclasping a pocket knife, which had been given him only the week before.

"I say, what a jolly knife," exclaimed Arthur, "I wish you would give it to me."

"I can't, indeed, Arthur, I would if I could, but you see my godfather sent it me, and mo-

ther particularly told me I must keep it." This
was a somewhat necessary injunction, as it was
a well-known fact that Ben could never keep
anything that belonged to him.

"Well, then, will you lend it me for a day or
two?"

"Oh yes, only mind you don't lose it, for
mother would be vexed."

"Never fear; I ain't so careless as some folks."

The next afternoon, just before school was
over, the Vicar came in, looking very grave, and
with him was Farmer Brookes, the great man of
the village. He was a very unusual visitor, and
he looked very angry and perturbed, and seemed
to be muttering to himself, and vowing vengeance against some person or persons unknown.

The Vicar looked anxiously at the boys. Farmer Brookes talked to the master, and at last
his excited tones were heard all over the school-
room.

"I'll have him in prison, sir, whoever he may
be, I can tell you, as surely as my name is
James Brookes."

The elder boys all looked sorely puzzled, and
the younger ones clung together, as though they
were afraid of being seized, and carried off to
prison in Farmer Brookes' strong clutches.

Then after a few minutes' pause, the Vicar spoke.

"My lads, something very sad has happened. Farmer Brookes has a beautiful apple tree in his garden, of which he is very proud. He was going to have picked the apples off it this morning to take to Colston Market, and when he went into his garden, he found every apple gone. A thief had got in in the night, or at least, some time after nine o'clock yesterday evening, and taken all the fruit away."

Again there was silence; the boys saw that there was more to come.

"We have a clue to the offender," continued the Vicar, "I hope and pray that he may not be found here; but Farmer Brookes is naturally annoyed, and he asked to be allowed to come here, and bring a knife with him, which was dropped by the thief under the apple tree as he hurried away. Will you show the boys the knife, if you please, Mr. Brookes?"

And the Farmer held up Ben's knife before the astonished lads. Not one of them spoke— they had all in turn admired it; but they all loved honest Ben, and not one of them could find it in their hearts to be his accuser.

It was to Ben himself that the Vicar spoke

first. And as he turned and looked at the boy, he was struck by the scared white look upon his face.

" Ben, do you know whose knife this is ?"

And in a low trembling voice came the answer, " It is mine, sir."

Farmer Brookes came forward now, and probably would have laid violent hands on poor Ben, if the Vicar had not held him back.

" You took my apples, did you, you young thief? You shall pay for it dearly, I promise you. How will you like three months in Colston jail ?"

" I did not take them," answered Ben, looking up this time into the Vicar's face.

" Then how did your knife get there ?"

Ben did not answer.

" Speak, my boy," said the Vicar, kindly ; " explain how your knife got under the apple tree, if you were not there."

" If you please, sir, I cannot."

Poor Ben ; there had come before him during those few moments a vision of Arthur Willis in prison, and his mother's heart broken : to save both mother and son from that he would bear anything.

The other boys were dismissed. Farmer

Brookes went away, the Vicar promising to see him again; and then the latter and the Master tried to get at the truth, but without success.

"I did not steal the apples, sir—I did not go near the garden; but I cannot explain how my knife got there."

He would not say one word more or less. And then the Vicar told him that until he spoke the truth—the whole truth—he must not come into the choir.

"I will say nothing about school," he said; "the holidays begin to-morrow, and perhaps before the four weeks have passed, you will have thought better of this."

He spoke severely for him; he was provoked at the seeming obstinacy exhibited by his favourite,—for Ben *was* a favourite with the Vicar, as he was with every one else.

And the poor boy looked into his face and said,

"When shall I go to prison, sir?"

"I don't know what Farmer Brookes may do, I cannot tell; but Ben, if you will only explain the thing—only confess—I can promise you that you shan't go to prison at all. Farmer Brookes will be satisfied, if you will only tell the truth."

"I have told all I can."

And the Vicar turned away, and sighed, and called Roger, to speak to him.

"Roger, do you know anything of this ?"

"No, sir, nothing."

"Where was Ben last night ?"

"He went after Church to take Mrs. Willis an egg that his bantam had laid. Oh, sir, he always would be Arthur's friend, although I told him harm would come of it ;" and Roger looked at the Vicar, as though he expected to be applauded for his discernment.

"Ben is a good, true lad," was the answer ; "I cannot do otherwise than I *have* done, because of the example to others, but I mean to believe in his innocence until he is proved to be guilty."

What was that that came upon Roger's face as the Vicar spoke ? was it—could it have been a shadow of disappointment ?

And then the boy went home ; and we have already seen the trouble that came to the little cottage on that sweet July evening.

As Ben was running wildly into the woods he met Arthur Willis.

"Oh, Arthur, Arthur," he cried, "I won't peach—I won't say a word—but my knife was found under Farmer Brookes' apple tree, and the Vicar has turned me out of the choir, and they are going to take me to prison, and oh what shall I do?"

Arthur's sallow cheek grew a shade paler as he answered, "To prison?"

"Yes; if I don't go, you must."

Then Arthur trembled violently, and cried, "Oh, Ben, Ben, 'twould kill mother; don't tell on me."

"I ain't going to; they may tear me in pieces, but I won't break your mother's heart, Arthur."

"Ben, I don't think there's any one like you, but will you swear it?"

"Yes—no, that would be wrong; my promise is as good as my oath." And there was something grand in the proud way in which honest Ben tossed back the curls from his forehead.

"Thank you," said Arthur, more humbly than Ben had ever heard him speak. And then he passed on, and left the boy kneeling beneath the trees, asking GOD to help him in his sorrow and his difficulty.

Those were sad weeks that followed that sweet summer evening. The truth had not been arrived at, and there was nobody in all Charleton who did not believe that Ben Mason was a thief, they were willing to own that he had not done it maliciously; probably his love of fun had led him into the garden, and then the spirit of mischief had triumphed over his better nature. Even the Vicar had his doubts now, and began to despair of his favourite's name ever being cleared.

Farmer Brookes was furious still, but he had a great respect for John Mason, and had desisted from pressing the charge against his boy.

And Ben knew what they all thought—knew that his father and mother, and Roger, all thought him guilty, and even his little brothers used to pity him and say, " Poor Ben, why are you naughty, Ben ?"

Then there came a day when a letter arrived at the cottage from Ben's godfather offering the lad a good situation in his office in London. " We'll get on so long as you are honest, my lad, I am quite sure."

" You can't go, Ben," said his father, sorrowfully; " and yet what a chance it is."

" No, father, I know I can't," had been the humble answer.

And then Roger said, " Father, may I go? you need not be afraid for me; you can trust me. I don't like teaching; I shall never do well here."

The godfather was written to, and he agreed to take Roger instead of Ben. And so it was settled that one day early in September Roger was to go to London.

He went to wish the Vicar good-bye; he stood before him happy and bright at his new prospects.

"Roger, my boy, do you remember the Ninth Sunday after Trinity?"

"No, sir; at least I don't know what you mean."

"I mean the words of the Epistle from which I preached that day, 'Let him that thinketh he standeth take heed lest he fall.' Roger, your great temptation is your self-confidence. I must speak to you plainly, my lad, to-day. I chose those words on that Sunday—the Sunday after poor Ben's disgrace—because I felt and knew what was in your mind, how you prided yourself upon the fact, that you could never have done that of which your brother was accused. My boy! I cannot bear to speak unkindly to you, to-day, but I want you to carry the words away with you into your new life. I asked my sister to illuminate them for you upon this card; will

you hang it up in your room, Roger? and ask
GOD to help you to know that you cannot stand
without Him, that if you trust only in your own
strength you must fall; will you think mercifully of Ben, and try to believe him innocent?"

"Yes, sir;" but somehow when Roger had
gone away, the Vicar did not feel happy about
him.

The months wore on; Ben was still under a
cloud, he never went back to school, but after
some difficulty he got a situation as gardener's
boy at the doctor's, at Colston.

He was never at home except in the early
morning and late at night, but on Sundays he
was always at Church; and his clear sweet voice
rose in chant, and psalm, and hymn, just as
it had done when he sat in his place in the
choir.

He never saw Arthur now; the boy seemed
to try to keep out of his way, and Ben heard
that his mother was much worse, and that hu-
manly speaking she could not live very long.

And poor Ben went on bearing the burden
that was so very hard to bear, and asking GOD
to help him.

One morning tidings of evil came to the little

cottage. Ben's godfather wrote and asked John Mason to take Roger home, because of his bad behaviour. "I can't manage him at all," he wrote; "he's given up all his good ways, he never goes to Church, and is always with bad companions, and I want to get him out of the way before he is led into worse mischief."

John Mason was ill in bed when that letter reached him.

"Ben," he said, when the boy came home that night, "you must go to London and bring your brother back."

Ben went, but it was too late to save Roger from what his employer had feared; he and some other boys had been taken up, for dishonest practices, and the magistrate had sent them to a Reformatory for three years, and poor Ben had to carry the bad news home.

"Both my boys disgraced," sighed the poor father; "oh, why am I punished like this?"

Ben's heart sank within him when he heard the words of agony. Must he bear it still— must he still keep silence. Yes; Widow Willis was dying, and he must spare her and save Arthur.

Another week, and the poor woman was laid in her grave; and the evening of her funeral

Arthur went to the Vicar and told the truth; and honest Ben's name was cleared, and just a little ray of sunshine broke through the gloom, which surrounded the inmates of that once cheerful cottage.

"I am ready to go to prison, sir," Arthur had said, but the Vicar took him to Farmer Brookes, and the hot-headed, but good-hearted fellow, forgave the boy, whose sorrow for his mother's loss was so evidently real.

"Please, sir, will you make me good like Ben?" and the good clergyman promised to do his best, and in the years that came afterwards Arthur Willis redeemed his character, and was a steady honest youth.

John Mason never recovered from his illness, (rheumatic fever); he lived on for a long time, but his limbs were paralyzed, and Ben worked hard and supported the rest of the family, and the happiest day to the youth in all the week was Sunday, when he sang GOD's praises in the choir, and knelt at the Holy Altar and fed upon the Heavenly Food.

One Sunday morning as he was kneeling in his accustomed place at the Early Celebration, the words of the Epistle fell upon his ears, "Let him that thinketh he standeth, take heed lest he fall," and mingled with those words, there came a sound as of a low choking sob; and Ben turned round to see from whence that sound proceeded, and his eyes fell upon Roger's face —as he too knelt humbly on his knees.

Yes; Roger had come home, the night before, too late to disturb his father and mother, and had slept out in the fields, and had gone to the Church he once had loved so well; and the text which ought to have been his watchword, came to him to add to his humility and self-reproach.

Ben took his brother home; and there was great joy in the cottage on that Ninth Sunday after Trinity, because he who had fallen so low had by GOD's mercy learned to stand again.

Dear children who have read this little tale, have you learned the lesson of humility it is meant to teach? Do you trust in your own strength? do you feel sure that you will never fall? Surely not, for we know that even GOD's own chosen Saints have sinned, and repented in very dust and ashes. It *is* hard always to stand, hard to battle against the waves of this troublesome world, but help is always near us; the Master's loving Arm is ever stretched out to keep us from falling, to raise us up when we have fallen, if we pray for His help and succour.

A HERO AND A HEROINE.

Tenth Sunday after Trinity.

"May faith each weak petition fill,
And waft it to the skies,
And teach our hearts 'tis goodness still
That grants it or denies."

HE was a very dirty grubby little boy indeed, this hero of mine, and as for my heroine, she was if possible more dirty and grubby still; for my hero's hair of course was short, whilst my heroine's unkempt locks hung down her back and over her face and into her eyes, in a way that added to her generally forlorn appearance.

I am afraid the description does not sound promising, or that my young readers will say that the title of my story is a very inappropriate one. Fancy calling such poor little things as this Dan and Mattie, of whom I am going to

v.   G

tell you, a hero and a heroine! why heroes
are people who fight battles, and do some wonderful thing; and heroines—well, heroines can't
fight, of course, at least it does not often come
into a woman's way to have to fire off a gun, or
draw a sword; but we have all of us read stories
of gentle ladies who by their brave, calm, resolute
deeds, have held a fortress against the enemy,
and we know how Sisters of Mercy have gone
into the battle-field, and braved unheard of
dangers, so that they might save the lives of the
wounded, and speak of hope to the dying.

Yes, all this is quite true, but I want to vin-
dicate the title of my tale, and to convince you
that Dan and Mattie have some claim to be
looked upon as a hero and a heroine.

It was on a Sunday afternoon that I first made
the acquaintance of the strange little pair. I
was on my way to take the service at the little
Mission Room, which had lately been opened
in the parish of S. Cuthbert, one of the poorest
and most densely populated parishes in all London, and as I passed through the streets on that
grilling August day, my heart sank within me,
as I heard the sounds of blasphemy which filled
the air, and as I· saw the traffic that was going
on, on that Day of Rest, the shops open, the

people bargaining and wrangling and quarrelling, as they stood and made their purchases, and tried to beat the vendors down to the lowest possible price.

"Will it ever be different?" I mused; "will the work that we have begun in faith and in hope end in success? Will the little Mission Room see one soul brought to the knowledge of its sin and of its guilt, and seeking for pardon through the Precious Blood?" And I asked GOD to help me in the work He had given me to do.

I was passing one of those small wretched looking shops, and something impelled me to pause for a few minutes, and listen to the conversation of a little ragged boy and girl, apparently about ten and twelve years of age, who stood gazing into the window, at the gaudy coloured prints which were displayed to view.

They were miserable looking creatures, pale and thin and wan; and yet with a certain brightness and intelligence in their young faces which somehow or other attracted me strangely.

" Look here, Mattie," said the boy; "look at this soldier fighting like a lion; and read what's written underneath, 'A real hero.'"

Mattie flattened her nose against the window

pane, thinking it right to get as near the picture as possible; but finding this plan did not answer, she retired a few paces, and gazed admiringly at the brilliant colouring which had so attracted Dan's attention.

"Ain't it beautiful?" she said. "Dan, I should like to be a hero, shouldn't you?"

"What a stupid you are," answered Dan; "why of course I should like to be one, but you couldn't—heroes are men, women never could be heroes."

"Yes, they could," responded Mattie, "I'm sure they could; I once read something about it in one of Mr. Tyler's books, and I mean to be a woman hero."

"Mattie, you're a goose," was the somewhat scornful reply; "you know well enough you couldn't fight as that fellow is fighting."

"No, I don't suppose I could," answered poor Mattie, looking it must be confessed somewhat crestfallen, "for of course I couldn't leave Tiny, it wouldn't do."

"Never mind," said Dan, with a patronising air, "you're a good girl, you are; Mr. Tyler says you're the best in the house. And when I'm a hero, won't I do a lot for you and for Tiny."

There rose to Mattie's cheek ever so faint a

tinge of colour as her brother spoke. It was pleasant to be praised by Dan, and the joys that came into the poor little girl's life were very few and far between.

At this moment the sound of the old cracked bell which summoned the poor people of that wretched locality to the Mission Service, began to ring.

" I say, Mattie, shall we come to Church ?"

" No," answered Mattie, despondingly, " 'tain't a bit of good, you know it ain't, Dan ; I've tried it all the week, and so have you, and I think she's been worse instead of better. No, prayers ain't no good at all, as I can see. You know the Parson said last week that GOD, Who lives up above the bright blue sky, would give us all we asked for, and I did think He would make Tiny well, and so did you, Dan ; and you see, we did ask Him, and she ain't a bit better, only worse."

" The Parson said we must ask Him rightly," replied Dan ; " perhaps we didn't know the right way ; perhaps if we was to go to-day we might hear it."

" No, I can't go, Tiny may want me."

" Nonsense, Mattie, Tiny is sure to be asleep for the next two hours ; you know she always does sleep all the afternoon, when she has had such a bad night as she had last night."

The bell had stopped by this time, and yet I felt loath to leave my hero and my heroine, without hearing more about them and about Tiny, whoever she might be. I had two little hymn-books in my hand, and I went up to them, and presented one to each of them, and I thought the dirty faces brightened as I did so, and Mattie said to Dan,

"I think perhaps Tiny won't be awake yet, and we'll go to Church for a bit."

"Where do you live?" I asked.

"Down in Bottle Court, just by the river."

"I should like to come and see you ; may I come?"

"Yes, if you please, sir," answered Mattie; "Dan is out all day,—he's in the collar trade, —and I goes out in the mornings and sells flowers, but I can't stay out all day, because of Tiny."

"Who is Tiny?"

"Our little sister, and she's always bad—never can move."

"And have you no father nor mother?"

"No, mother died just after Tiny was born ; and father—" and I thought the child's voice trembled as she spoke—"and father's gone away to look for work."

"How shall I find you? Bottle Court is a large place."

"Ask for Dan Smith, everybody knows Dan," replied Mattie, with just the smallest air of pride in her brother, in her voice and manner. "You'll see a door just opposite you as you come into the Court, and in the window there's Mr. Tyler's name put up—Hezekiah Tyler, shoemaker; if you asks him he'll show you our room."

"Very well, I will come soon."

I hurried on, and saw my two little friends coming slowly after me, reading out of their hymn books as they walked along.

In a few minutes, the short simple service began; a metrical Litany, a few Collects, and some bright cheerful hymns. Then I spoke to those poor people as I always did on Sunday afternoons, as earnestly and simply as I could, about the things that belonged unto their peace.

I saw those two sharp eager little faces looking at me intently, and it seemed to me as though I could help them to understand things better than they had done before. I will just tell you very shortly some of the words I said.

It was the Tenth Sunday after Trinity, and I said the Collect over very slowly, and tried to explain it to them.

"Let Thy merciful ears, O LORD, be open to the prayers of Thy humble servants, and that they may obtain their petitions, make them to ask such things as shall please Thee; through JESUS CHRIST our LORD. Amen."

"My dear friends, GOD is always ready to hear your prayers; not the shortest most simple words of a little child are lost upon Him; He never closes His ears to the supplications of His own people. For it was to save us all—to save you and me and all the world—that JESUS came to die upon the Cross; but He bade us pray to GOD in His name, and to ask Him to take us to heaven. If we do not pray, GOD will not give us the blessings He has promised us; if we do pray there is nothing He will keep back from us—nothing at least that is good for us. For this is the lesson of to-day's Collect, that GOD would teach us to ask such things as shall please Him. We do not know what is good for ourselves, or for each other; the very trials that seem so hard to bear, are sent us by our loving FATHER Who is in Heaven, and we must not ask Him to take them from us. We must ask

Him to give us patience, and love and faith to bow to whatever He thinks right.

"Perhaps some of you have some loved one at home, who is very ill, suffering great pain, and you have asked GOD to take away the illness, and to make your father or mother, or your little brother or sister quite well. GOD *has* heard your prayers, my friends, be sure of that, and in some way or other He has answered them, but not as you in your ignorance and your blindness wished. It did not please Him to raise your loved one from the sick bed, it was His Will to let the suffering go on, perhaps to make the poor sick weary soul long for the joys of Heaven.

"My children, pray still earnestly, truly, faithfully, only be sure that you are asking what will please GOD. You will tell me perhaps that you do not know what will please Him. JESUS left us that most perfect prayer which we all of us know, and in that prayer He tells us to say, 'Thy Will be done,' and that is what we must say,—we must ask Him if it be His Will to do such and such things for us, and if it be not His Will we must pray for patience both for ourselves and for others. We are sure, quite sure that this will please GOD, and that in His own

most gracious way,—and His way alone is right,
—He will hear and answer our petitions.

"My friends, you have all of you heard of
the great deeds done by GOD's Saints and Mar-
tyrs,—do you know how they found strength to
bear all their troubles? It was just by praying
to GOD, and asking Him not for any one special
thing, but that in all things they might please
Him, and do His Will. And you can follow in
the footsteps of the Saints if you will only in all
things submit yourselves to the Will of GOD; if
you will try to ask of Him only such things as
shall please Him."

Once or twice as I spoke, I glanced towards
the bench where my hero and my heroine sat,
and I saw that they understood what I was saying, and that it was helping them ever so little
in their difficulties. I felt that I must know
more of them before long, and determined if
possible to go and see them on the following
evening.

I put my intention into execution. I knew
Bottle Court well; it was one of the worst
places in the whole of S. Cuthbert's Parish, and
I had heard my fellow-curates tell numerous
anecdotes of having been pelted with cabbage

stalks and egg shells, when on one or two occa-
sions they had attempted to invade its precincts.

I armed myself with a stout stick by way of
precaution, and sallied forth to visit my little
friends.

I saw Hezekiah Tyler's name stuck up in a
window, and I knocked at the door, and received permission to enter. There stood before
me the very quaintest little old man I had ever
seen,—a man with a long body, and no legs at
all that I could detect, although a pair of very
large feet were plainly discernible.

It was a yellow, puckered-up old face upon
which I gazed, and yet there was a merry
twinkle in the grey eyes, and a smile about the
large mouth which impressed me much in
Hezekiah's favour in spite of the peculiarity of
his appearance.

"Good evening," I said; "will you be kind
enough to tell me where I can find Dan Smith
and his little sister?"

"Yes, surely, sir, and glad enough I am that
the poor things has found a friend like you;
they sorely needs it, sir, and on the whole they're
good children as children goes now-a-days."

Then the old man made me sit down upon a
little low stool, the only article of furniture be-

sides a bedstead, and a bench which was covered with boots and shoes and cobbling materials, of which his poor room boasted, and he told me as much as he knew of my hero and my heroine's history.

It was pretty much the same as they had told me the day before, only Hezekiah added a great many facts which they had suppressed.

"They comed here about three years agone, and took the little loft out in the back yard. Their father brought them; he was a bad man if ever there was one, was Frank Smith; his wife had not been dead more than a week when they comed, and the poor little uns was very low and sad. There's one as you haven't seen, sir, Tiny, a cripple, but the sweetest little lass as you can set eyes upon. Well, Frank Smith went out all day long, and left his children to fish for themselves, and when he did come home sometimes 'twould have been better if he had stayed away. They bore it all patient enough, poor things, and they managed to pick up a bit of work, and on that they lives, and keeps poor Tiny. Six months agone the father went away, and he's never been seen nor heard of since; he said he was going to find some work, but somehow I don't think he'll ever come back, he's what you may call, sir, an unnatural parient."

I certainly agreed with this view of the case, and Hezekiah went on.

" They told me as how they had been to your service yesterday, sir, and I had a mind to try it myself; it's many and many a long year since I was inside a Church; and I'm thinking it can't be very long before this poor old body is carried there to have the last prayers read over it, and 'twould be better if I tried to get ready before the end comes. I knows it's late, sir," said the poor old fellow, brushing his horny hand across his eyes; "but GOD is very good, and till lately there never was a Church to go to in these parts, except what was filled by the gentry; and last night when I heard them children a-telling how you had spoke about GOD's Will, and about saying our prayers, and asking for right things, why then I thought I'd just come and ask you to help me a bit."

A feeling of intense thankfulness was in my heart as the old man spoke; thankfulness that my poor words had been of use to anybody.

I sat upon that rickety stool for a long time, and talked to Hezekiah; I think he would have liked to keep me there for hours, but the shades of evening were fast closing around us, and I was obliged to ask him to take me to the loft where my hero and my heroine lived.

Such a place as it was; up an old tumble-down staircase that seemed to sway beneath my feet as I ascended it carefully; and through a low door, against which by the way I gave my head a tremendous bump, and then into a—what shall I call it?—not a room, not a loft, a kind of upper dungeon, where, sitting in a corner on a heap of straw, I detected Dan and Mattie.

They both rose at the sight of me, and both exclaimed, "Here's Tiny, sir."

Where Tiny was was a difficult matter to discover, but old Hezekiah had armed himself with a candle and a match, and soon the faint light streamed upon the very palest, thinnest little face I had ever seen, lying down on the straw and smiling a bright pleasant little smile.

"It's the Parson, Tiny, as we told you of."

And Tiny held out her poor little hand, and said, "Good evening, sir."

"Here's a chair," said Dan, "I've been mending it on purpose for you, sir; but be kind enough to sit down as gently as you can, for it would have been better for an extra nail or two."

I did as I was bid, but with all my precautions my weight was too much for the old chair, and down I fell, to the evident amusement of Hezekiah, Mattie, and Tiny, but somewhat to the discomfiture of poor Dan.

I jumped up and made the best of it, and then I began to talk to the children about their daily lives, and their prospects of work, and whilst we were talking Tiny fell asleep, her head resting on Mattie's shoulder.

"There, she's quite comfortable now," said the little elder sister, looking lovingly into the puny face; "may be she'll sleep five or six hours now if I don't move."

"But you will be tired," I said, "you will want to go to sleep yourself."

"No, I shan't, and if I do, I can just manage to get a minute or two at a time sitting up like this, it's the only way she can get any rest sometimes, poor little dear, when her breathing is so bad; and then when she wakes up Dan will take her, and that's how we divides our nights."

It was all said quite cheerfully without any effort, or any idea that she was doing anything at all out of the way, and Dan chimed in and added,

"We're so strong and hearty, nothing hurts us."

"Perhaps," I said, "God in His mercy will make Tiny better soon."

The brother and sister looked at each other then, and Mattie said, "Tell him about it, Dan," but Dan looked shy, and it was the girl who spoke at last,

"If you please, sir, we hadn't been to Church before last Sunday week not for ever so long, not since a long, long time before mother died; she used to take us sometimes, but then our clothes got bad,—and we have forgotten to say our prayers,—and then when we was walking along and heard the bell, we thought we should like to go in, because we saw lots of boys and girls just as ragged and dirty as we are going in, and you said, sir, God would hear us if we said our prayers, and we did, and we asked Him to make Tiny well; and all through the week she only got worse, so yesterday I didn't want to go to Church till you gave us the hymn-books, and looked so kind like, and I'm glad we went, and so is Dan, because you talked about God's Will and about asking what pleased Him, and Dan and I have been saying that perhaps it don't please Him to make Tiny well, and so we must bear it."

I put my hand upon the rough head, and in my heart I thanked GOD that the teaching I had tried to give my poor people on that Tenth Sunday after Trinity, had already brought forth some fruit.

I was revolving in my mind whether it would be possible to get any work for Dan which would pay better than the "collar trade," which I gleaned was anything but a profitable` calling, and I said, "What would you like to be, Dan?"

"I don't know, sir, I ain't sure."

"I knows," ejaculated Mattie.

"Well, little woman, speak out."

"I knows what we both wants to be—heroes; that's the word, like the soldier in the picture shop, and like the people as I have read of in Mr. Tyler's books—we can read Mr. Tyler's books, mother learned us to before she went away."

I could not resist a smile, and yet I felt that in their little lives of self-sacrifice, in their great love and care for Tiny, they were in their own small way something of a hero and a heroine, fighting and trusting, and bearing all things patiently.

A sudden thought struck me. "Dan," I said, "I don't know that I can get you made a little soldier; a little sailor wouldn't do as well, would it?"

Oh, how the grimy face brightened up at the bare suggestion of such a thing, how poor Dan clapped his hands and said, "Oh, please send me to sea, sir, I've always wanted to go."

Then there was a little sob from the bed, and I saw Mattie's face buried in Tiny's lank light hair.

The boy heard the sound, and sprang to his sister's side, "No, no, Mattie, I won't leave you, I won't go."

"Yes, you will, Dan, if the Parson can get you a place."

"We will see about it," I said, almost sorry that I had spoken, for poor Mattie's face was very white, and I saw her bite her lip to keep the tears back. I bade the children good-bye, promising to send a lady to see Tiny, and to find out what would be best for her.

"I will come again soon," I said, "before Sunday; in the mean time if you want anything come to the Clergy House and ask for me."

The next morning I was told that a little flower girl was waiting to speak to me; I knew at once who my visitor was, and said that she was to be shown up to my room.

In another minute Mattie made her appearance: "If you please, sir, I hope you'll not be angry, but I wanted to ask you a favour."

"Well, my child, what is it? I will do anything I can for you, you may be quite sure."

The poor swollen eyes that told of a sleepless night were raised trustingly to my face, and Mattie said, "Dan do want to go to sea, sir, oh, so bad."

"Well, I will do my best to get him there."

"Yes, but 'tain't that; you see we talked about it a long long time last night after you was gone, and he said he wouldn't leave me, and so I've come to ask you to tell him as how it would be best for us both, and I can take care of Tiny, and GOD will show me the way to ask what is best for her."

"Mattie," I said, "can you bear your brother to leave you?"

The long pent up sorrow found vent at last, and Mattie sat down upon the floor and sobbed as though her poor little heart would break.

I did not try to comfort her then; and at last she looked up and said, "GOD will help me to bear it. I know it will be awful hard, but it will do him good, and it's what he wishes and

perhaps it will make a hero of him, like Lord
Nelson in Mr. Tyler's book."

So it was all settled. I had a naval friend in
town just then, and I saw him and arranged
everything satisfactorily, and before another
fortnight had elapsed Dan had gone to Ports-
mouth to join his ship. I took him to the sta-
tion myself, and so I was present at the parting,
and never, so long as I live, shall I forget that
day.

Tiny was sitting up in an invalid chair that
we had managed to get for her, and Dan and
Mattie were standing on either side of her.

"I'll bring you back a beautiful singing bird,
Tiny, from over the seas," said Dan in a choking
voice.

And Tiny smiled her own little sweet smile
and said, "You'll come home soon, Dan, to
Mattie and to me."

"Yes, soon, very soon," answered Mattie, for
poor Dan could not speak, "and we'll say our
prayers, and ask GOD to take care of us all; and
Dan will say his prayers on board the big ship."

"Dan, we must be off," I said, and the poor
boy put his arms round his little crippled sister,
and I thought I heard him say a little prayer as
he bent over her.

And then he bade Mattie good-bye.

"Take care of yourself," he said, "and of her," and then he ran quickly down the old staircase, and I found him in Hezekiah's room crying like a baby.

"You'll be good to them, Mr. Tyler, won't you?" he said.

And Hezekiah only cried too, and I stood outside the door fearing to make a goose of myself.

The old cobbler told me afterwards that all through that day Mattie had kept running in and out of his place to hide her tears from Tiny.

"It wouldn't do to make her sorry, poor little dear," she had said, "she don't understand it like I do, she thinks he's a-coming back tomorrow, and she's looking forward to having the bird from over the seas."

The winter that followed was a very hard one; I had managed to persuade Hezekiah to move out of Bottle Court to a more healthy region, not far from the Mission Room, and Mattie and Tiny moved too, up into an attic where Tiny said she could see the blue sky, and it seemed as if she was nearer the Angels there.

And Mattie worked very hard; she had left

the flower trade; she said it wasn't a good business, and she had got some shirts from a slop shop, and there she sat at sewing all the day long; only thinking of how she could get Tiny all she wanted, how she could brighten the little sick child's life.

Tiny did not get any better, and her nights were very bad, and sometimes she was very fretful in the day time, and Mattie bore all her burden alone, only asking GOD to help her to be patient, and sometimes adding a little prayer, which was, that she might see Dan before very long, "but only if it pleases GOD," she said, "if it don't please Him I will not ask it."

Often in the early morning, and in the evening, when Tiny was asleep, Hezekiah and the little girl used to kneel side by side in the Mission Room : he to try and get ready for his long journey, she to pray for strength to do her duty in her lonely life.

Tidings had come to the child of her father's death ; he had started in an emigrant ship bound for Australia ; the vessel had been wrecked, and Frank Smith's name was amongst those who had perished in the waves.

Poor Mattie shed a few tears when Hezekiah read the news to her out of a paper that was at least a month old. "I've only Dan and Tiny now," she said, "and Tiny has only me to take care of her; I must work harder than ever."

And my little heroine did work ever so bravely, and the months passed on, and it seemed to me that Tiny's cheeks had a little more colour in them, and Tiny's legs were a little stronger; the summer waned, and autumn came, and then winter, and one Christmas Day I saw a face in the little Church (we had a Church now) which I hardly recognized; it was so brown and bright, and ruddy; but the sailor's dress, and Mattie's beaming eyes told me who the new comer was; and when service was over Mattie and Dan waited for me in the porch. The boy could hardly speak for joy at being at home again, but Mattie spoke for him : " Oh, sir, he's a real live hero, he jumped into the sea after a boy, and saved his life, and he has a big medal telling all about it; and Tiny's got a real live bird, will you come and see it ?"

I walked home with my hero and my heroine, and there I found Tiny sitting in Hezekiah's room, and a bright yellow canary was warbling its own sweet song, and Tiny said, " Oh, ain't God good to give us Dan again?" And Dan,

who had found his tongue by this time, said,
" It's the happiest day as ever was—but I think
the best day was when you told us about praying
rightly, sir, it seems as if all the good had come
to us since then."

HARRY'S WREATH.

"How wilt thou then look back and smile,
On thoughts that bitterest seem'd erewhile,
And bless the pangs that made thee see,
This was no world of rest for thee."

"YOU may as well stand on one side, Ada,
there's not a chance for you; I cannot
think how it is you have tried for the prize; you
know you never can do anything."

"Yes, I know it," was the meek gentle answer, "but Harry, my brother, who is so ill,
wanted me to try, and he has helped me so, all
through the long summer evenings, and he will
want to know how many marks I have—that is
the only reason why I wanted to hear when they
were called out."

It was examination day at the Middle Class

v.   H

School, kept by the Sisters of S. Agatha, in the town of Burlington. The summer holidays were over; for some reason the examination had had to be postponed until the girls re-assembled; and now it was to be decided who was the winner of the first class prize for general knowledge.

There were four or five contending for it, and all so nearly equal in many ways, that it was a very hard matter to decide who was likely to carry it off; there was one who had worked hard, and plodded on with exemplary diligence, but the verdict had gone forth amongst her schoolfellows that she had not a chance of success. And that one was Ada Somerville, whose brother Harry was so anxious that she should do her best, and whose poor little heart was beating with excitement now as she stood amongst the eager crowd, all waiting to hear the names called out.

She was a little pale meek-looking girl, with nothing at all remarkable about her appearance; her hair was sandy, and her face was freckled, and most people if they had said anything at all about her, would probably have pronounced her plain and uninteresting-looking; it was only those who knew and loved Ada who saw something that belonged to her alone, in that strangely rare smile which would come sometimes and light up the somewhat heavy face—and that smile never came there because she herself was pleased; it was only to be seen when some good or some pleasure had come to another. Her life was not a very bright one; her father was dead, her mother had married again, and Harry, her only brother, was always ill, and unable to follow his profession, that of a lawyer. There was a small family of step-brothers and sisters, and Ada knew that as time went on, she should have to be the bread-winner, and go out into the world and earn money for Harry and for herself.

It was the one trial of Harry's life that this should be the case, it required all the youth's faith to bow to the decree that had made him almost helpless, and that would necessitate Ada's working for herself and for him.

Mr. Stafford, their step-father, was a good kindly conscientious man, but his own stipend as clerk in a large mercantile house, was barely sufficient for the wants of his increasing family, and although he tried hard to do his best for Harry and Ada, he did not think it fair to keep from them that at no very distant day the little timid shrinking sister must do something for herself. And because of this it was that Ada had worked so hard for the prize.

"Of course I shan't win it, Harry," she had said, "but the work will do me good, and will teach me a great deal that I ought to know." And Harry had quite agreed with her, and all through the lengthening spring evenings, and far on into the bright summer nights, the brother and sister would sit plodding over their books, he the patient teacher, she the docile pupil.

And now the day had come, and Ada in her white dress, and the blue ribbon which Harry had given her round her neck, stood and waited, as we have already said, to hear the result of the adding up of the marks.

At her side was a girl somewhere about her own age, a proud imperious-looking maiden, upon whose very pretty face there was a look of flushed pleasurable excitement. Her name was Millicent Grey, and somehow or other it had got abroad that morning that she had won the prize.

She it was who had begged poor Ada to stand out of the way, and who had told her that there was not a chance for her.

And we have seen how meekly Ada bore the

somewhat scornful words; and then as some
one else pushed past her, she retired to a distant
form and sat there, not thinking of herself—self
was a subject that did not often trouble Ada,—
but wondering what Harry was doing; trusting
that he had not allowed one single hope to linger
in his heart, she was almost afraid he had; he
had laughed so merrily when she kissed him and
bade him good-bye, and he had said that he
was going out into the garden to weave a crown
of flowers, in case she should require it when she
came home victorious.

Her mother was not well, and could not be
present, as the other girls' mothers were, and
her sole escort was her little step-brother, Charlie,
a merry urchin of some seven or eight years old,
who kept very close to her side, and who now
announced in a loud whisper that he was glad she
had got nearer the door, as he should run off
and tell Harry that she had got the prize directly
the fact was announced.

"Please, Charlie, don't speak so, you know it
is quite out of the question; did you not hear
Millicent Grey say just now, that I never could
do anything?"

"Millicent Grey is a stuck up—"

The rest of the not very complimentary sentence was checked by Ada's hand being placed tightly across Charlie's mouth.

There came a low murmur, a pause of expectation, and the Sister in charge of S. Agatha's school proceeded to read the report.

On the whole it was a very creditable one; several prizes were awarded to the juniors, the first class girls had to wait to the last to hear their fate.

When their turn came it was rather a long business; most of them had done well; five or six remarkably so; one in geography; one in history; Millicent Grey had specially distinguished herself in both these subjects, and on the whole all her papers were remarkably good, but there was another who had done better still, whose work was altogether more careful and comprehensive, and that one was—

"Hurrah!" shouted a voice that might have been the voice of a youthful Stentor. "Ada, don't sit there like a stick or a stone."

"Charlie, dear Charlie, do be quiet, who is it has the prize? is it not Millicent Grey?"

"You duffer," loudly rejoined the incorrigible Charlie, "why it's yourself. Ada Somerville is your name, isn't it? I'm off to tell Harry."

"My child," said a sweet low voice at the

girl's side, "my child, I am so glad, you must go now, they are calling you to receive your prize."

Ada did not move. "Oh, Sister Kate, surely it is a mistake, it cannot be true."

Again the name sounded through the room; and this time, led by Sister Kate, Ada went forward, and the handsomely bound volumes were put into her hands.

"Ada, you richly deserve them; you have worked very hard, and I have had no fault of any kind to find with you."

Ada murmured some low words of thanks, and as she went back to her place there was that smile upon her face, which made her look almost pretty. Even then, in the moment of her triumph, her thoughts were of Harry and her mother, and when Sister Kate said, "Are you not glad, dear?" the answer came in low tremulous tones: "Oh, yes, I cannot help it, they will be so glad," and then the smile went away, and a troubled look came upon her brow; she had seen Millicent's dark eyes fixed upon her face, with a look in them that pained her little tender heart. And the thought would come into her mind, "I have gained the prize, but I have made an enemy; she never liked me, she looked then as though she hated me."

For the most part the girls were glad that Ada had carried the day; they all thought her a good little thing, and they knew all about Harry, and Charlie's excitement had amused them immensely; they called him a duck and a darling, and all kinds of gushing epithets in which the young ladies of the present day indulge; the others, whose names had received honourable mention, came forward generously and congratulated the victor; there was only one who stood aloof, and that one was Millicent Grey.

It was always the custom to end such days at S. Agatha's with a service in the Sisters' beautiful Chapel, and the Warden generally gave a short address at the end of it.

On that August evening he spoke on the Gospel for the week, (the eleventh after Trinity,) and he told his hearers of the deep lesson to be learned from the blessed words of our own dear LORD, in the Parable of the Pharisee and the Publican.

" My children," he said, " I dare say you have heard this Gospel read Sunday after Sunday and day after day, and you have heard it, I hope and think, reverently, because you know Who it is Who spoke the words,—He Who spake as never man spake,—but yet I doubt whether you have taken it to heart as you ought to have done; you have felt that you did not like that proud self-sufficient Pharisee, all your sympathy has been given to the humble, lowly publican, who asked GOD's mercy for the many sins of his life. It has never entered into your heads to think that the sin of the Pharisee may be your sin; that because you do not stand apart and proclaim your goodness publicly, any one can accuse you of doing as he did.

" My children, I do not want to be hard upon you to-night of all nights, but I want you to look deep down into your hearts, and ask yourselves one little question, 'Have I ever looked down upon one of my companions? have I ever been angry because another was praised or put before me? has any thought of uncharitableness or envy come to me when I heard that what I had hoped would be mine, what I had tried for with all my might, had been awarded to some one else? have I fancied myself superior to my companions, and not confessed my pride when I found that they had in many ways excelled me?'

" Dear children, you will believe that I am speaking only in general terms, touching upon a sin that I think is very likely to find its way

into a school like this,—I pray that I may be
wrong. Every day when I offer the most holy
Sacrifice I ask that you may be pure and good
and true, all that Christian maidens ought to be.

"And, my children, I want you *all* to be *first*
—first in winning the great prize, even the prize
of the Heavenly Jerusalem. One more little
word you must take away with you to-night,—
do your best, your very best; never mind the
consequences, never fear the results; do all,
every little thing that comes to you to do, to
the glory of GOD; and then no thought of vain-
glory can come into your minds, and the sin of
the proud Pharisee will find no place in your
hearts."

The girls went to their homes in silence after
that solemn service was over. There was a
wreath of bright flowers lying on the table near
Harry's couch when Ada leant over him to receive his loving kiss.

"My little woman," he said, "I am so glad."

"And I am glad too, Harry; but please do
not let us talk of it to-night, because it is better
not, and because of the Warden's sermon."

He understood something of what she meant,
and he sent her to her mother's room, and said,

"The wreath can wait until to-morrow,

Birdie," (it was his pet name for her, rarely used,) and she gave him another kiss, and murmured some little loving words of gratitude for all he had done for her.

She went to her mother then, and afterwards to her good honest step-father, and they told her of their joy, but she was very quiet, and very still; a shadow seemed to have fallen upon her ever since she had seen that look upon Millicent Grey's face, and only something of the bright smile came back as she looked at merry rosy Charlie lying in his little bed; whilst on the pillow was a piece of paper, and scrawled upon it were the words, " They would not let me sit up, so I have written Hip, hip, hurrah !"

The light of the August moon fell upon Ada as she knelt before a plain wooden cross, and said her evening prayers, and examined herself with scrupulous care as to the sins and short-comings of the day that was past.

And then when this was done,—when the depths of the earnest conscientious nature had been, as it were, sounded,—the girl's head was bent very low, and she asked GOD to help her to be less like the Pharisee, less self-confident, and less conceited; for there had come into her mind the remembrance of a thought that had obtruded itself that night in the Chapel, of a moment when she had forgotten her mother and Harry, and every one but herself, and when she had caught sight of Millicent's pretty face, and there had been in her heart a feeling of triumph at having won the prize from the girl who had so often taunted her with her ignorance and stupidity.

"I must not wear Harry's wreath to-morrow, I must not let them make too much of me, or what has made us all so glad might turn into a danger and a snare."

The next morning when the fresh wreath of lovely flowers was placed lovingly upon Ada's head by Harry, she put it gently away, and said,

"I must not wear it yet, darling, put it away until I deserve it better, it would make me vain and conceited now."

"But it will be faded before you gain any more laurels, Ada."

"Yes, but I should like it put away and kept, please."

And Harry granted the somewhat strange request, and locked the chaplet away in his own room.

The light of that same August moon, which

had shone upon Ada Somerville, shone too
upon Millicent Grey as she knelt upon her
knees to ask GOD to lighten the darkness that
was coming.

Mechanically she said the words of her usual
prayers; but evil thoughts were in the girl's
heart that night; thoughts of anger against Ada,
of vexation that any one had done better than
she had, above all that stupid ugly Ada Somerville; and then she lay down upon her little
bed, and her father and mother came in, (Millicent was their only darling,) and gave her one
last loving kiss, and bade her not worry at her
ill-success, and predicted that next year all
would be right. She tried to smile, and to return their affection, but when they left her she
kept awake for a long time looking upon the
silvery moonbeams, and upon the twinkling
stars, as they came out one by one to cast their
brightness upon the earth, ever present types of
GOD's watchfulness and care. Millicent saw
them, and fixed her eyes upon them, but her
thoughts were very far away.

" I know it was not fair," she mused, " I know
it is quite impossible that left to herself she
could have done better than I did; it was that
brother of hers whom she is always talking about

who helped her to the prize, I have no doubt
he did half her papers; I shall keep a sharp look-
out next year, I can tell her, I am not going to
be humbled in this way again by such a little
stupid as that Ada Somerville."

No memory of the Warden's words was in
poor Millicent's mind then, no thought of the
sin of which he had warned the girls that evening, no prayer for help was on her heart nor on
her lips as she gave way to her angry jealous
feelings.

Time passed on, as time always does, whether
we wish it or not; there was very little outward
change in the lives of those two girls whose
story we are telling. Ada worked as hard as
ever, and Harry helped her, and the loving
little sister fancied that her brother was not
quite as strong as he had been a year before,
and sometimes the thought of the future, and of
having to leave him and go far away amongst
strangers would weigh upon the girl's heart, and
unfit her for a time for her present duties,—but
only for a time; she knew where to find strength,
and she would go to her little room and come
out bright and cheerful, to be Harry's friend and
companion.

Charlie grew a more incorrigible pickle than

ever, and there was another little baby in the
house ; and Ada felt that the sooner she could
get out into the world and earn some money for
herself the better it would be.

She was fifteen now; many girls she knew
had managed to get situations as nursery gover-
nesses before that, and Sister Kate, to whom
she had told her wish, had promised to look
out for something to suit her when she went
home at Easter.

And of Millicent there is little to tell. She
too worked hard, and she very seldom spoke to
Ada, and when she did it was generally in a
scornful way, which the other took as meekly as
was her wont. One change had come into both
the young lives, the very greatest that can come
to GOD's own baptised children.

The Bishop had not been to Burlington for
three years, until that Christmas after our story
begins. Then Ada and Millicent had been
confirmed, and had knelt side by side at the
Altar of GOD, and received the Holy Eucharist.
On Christmas Day it was that "the greatest
blessing life can give" came to those two, and
to many of their companions.

It was a stormy, rainy day, and when the
sacred service was over, most of the congrega-

tion stood in the porch, waiting for a drenching shower to cease.

Ada found herself at Millicent's side.

That day of all days, it seemed to her as though all must be peace and love and good will; she slipped her hand into the other girl's, and looked into her face, and said, " Kiss me, please, Millicent."

But Millicent tossed her head, and said, " There is my hand, that is enough; I hate kissing."

In the months that came afterwards, Millicent Grey remembered that cold Christmas morning, and the look that was upon Ada's face as she turned away to try and hide her disappointment.

The prize to be given at S. Agatha's this year was for arithmetic, that is to say, that was the subject to which the first class girls were specially asked to give their attention; there would be other rewards, of course, but this would be the best.

Millicent Grey's heart sank within her when she heard the news. She had never been fond of figures, and now she knew there was not a chance for her; and she was equally aware that sums had always been Ada's strong point, and that there was every probability that she would again carry off the prize.

"I should not mind if it were one of the others," mused Millicent, "Mary Ormond, or Annie Lander, or any of those, but I cannot and will not see Ada put before me again, it is more than I can bear."

She had been taught her duties, this poor child, ever since she could understand them, and you know the great inestimable helps that had come to her at Christmas; she knew as well as any one what was right, but she had not knelt humbly before GOD, she had not stood afar off, and asked for mercy; she had trusted in her own strength, she had made a boast of her own talents, and when the hour of trial came, and when temptation assailed her, she failed, just as we must all fail if we do not ask GOD to give us such a measure of His grace, that we, running the way of His commandments, may obtain His gracious promises, and be made partakers of the heavenly treasure.

The thought of doing Ada any real wrong did not come to Millicent for a very long time. It was one bright June day, just before the holidays began, that the tempter whispered in her

ear, and she in her pride and self-conceit, listened
to his subtle arguments.

Upon a desk in the school-room, probably
laid there by one of the Sisters who was hurriedly passing through, was a key to the arithmetic book which was in use at S. Agatha's.
Millicent was alone; her home was at some
little distance, and she had brought her luncheon
to school that day. Her first thought was to
open the book, and study the parts in which she
felt she had made mistakes. There was no
time to lose; the sums were to be given in
that afternoon; the girl looked at the clock,
it only wanted a quarter to three, and she
heard the pattering of many feet in the lobby
beyond.

No word of prayer rose to the poor child's
lips; only the tempter's voice spoke on, and
Millicent listened eagerly and willingly.

When one of the other girls came in she was
sitting at her desk, and looked, as Mary Ormond remarked, as white and scared as if she
had seen a bogie.

There was somewhat of a change in the ar-
rangements relative to the prizes this year; they
were not to be presented until after the holidays,
but the result of the examination was to be told

to the children that afternoon. The arithmetic papers had been given in that morning.

It was very late, past four o'clock, when Sister Agnes appeared, and it seemed to the girls as though there was on her sweet face an anxious perturbed expression.

" My dears, I want to tell you about the prizes at once ;" and she read out the names of all the successful competitors, and then she came to the arithmetic prize.

" There is one paper perfectly done," she said, and some of those girls who loved her so well thought that her voice sounded very sorrowful, " that one is Ada Somerville's."

There was a pause, and Sister Agnes continued, " I have lost the key to the arithmetic book, it really is of no consequence, except that it is one of my strictest rules that it should never be out of my desk, and it is gone. I am sure I had it last evening ; Sister Kate thinks she saw it this morning. Will you all look into your desks, dears—I will trust you to do it—and see if it is there ?"

They all did as she bade them. There was a little cry, a start of amazement from Ada Somerville's neighbour, for the missing book was in her desk.

If it had been found in possession of one of the others whose sums were wrong, probably none of the girls would have attributed the circumstance to any other cause than mere accident; as it was, every eye was fixed upon poor Ada, and she cowered and trembled beneath the astonished gaze.

"Ada, dear, can you explain this?"

"No, indeed, I cannot."

"The prize then must be in abeyance until after the holidays; it is very painful for me to have to say this, but I must have time to inquire into things. You must come to my room after school."

She went, shy and timid, as usual; and Sister Agnes was troubled at her manner. The truth was, the poor girl had met Millicent Grey in the passage on her way to Sister Agnes' room, and the look of triumph upon her face had startled the child out of her senses.

"My child, I must think what is to be done."

"Please, oh please don't tell Sister Kate's friends; she told me only this morning that she thought she had found a situation for me, and I was to go in August, and I do want so much to work for Harry, and mother, and the little ones."

And Sister Agnes kissed the pale face and said, " My child, I will ask GOD to help me to be just."

It was a sad going home for poor Ada. Harry was waiting at the door, holding in his hand the faded wreath.

" Are you to be crowned to-day, sister mine ?" he asked, playfully.

But she looked up into his face and said, " Oh, Harry," and he knew that there must be something very wrong, to make her speak in that tone.

In very few words she told her story, and they all made light of it, and said the mistake must soon be explained, and all would be right.

" I shouldn't mind so much if it were not for what Sister Kate said; I do so want to go and work for you all."

Her mother looked at her with tears in her eyes. The poor little fragile girl looked strangely unfit to go forth alone, and fight the battle of life.

Ere another week had passed, Ada was lying on a bed of sickness. It was an attack of measles, a complaint which had been very prevalent in the town, a very mild one, and the doctor said she would be up in a week.

And so she was, but somehow she did not regain her strength; all through the bright July days she lay upon the couch in Harry's room, and there was a far away look in her eyes which sent a strange thrill of fear to her mother's and brother's heart.

Sister Agnes had gone away for the holidays, and nothing more was heard of the book, and Ada was far too weak to think of taking a situation in August. She had better rest until Christmas, they all said.

August came, and she was much worse; her cough was very bad, and day by day her strength failed her, and the doctor shook his head, and did not give much hope that she would ever be well.

It was a Sunday afternoon, the Eleventh Sunday after Trinity, and Harry was sitting by his darling, when there came a low knock at the door. He opened it, and a girl brushed past him, and knelt at Ada's side.

" Oh Ada, Ada, I have been to Church, and it was the Gospel about the Pharisee and the Publican, and I heard you were very ill, and I have come to tell you I put the book into your desk; I always thought myself better and more clever than you are. Ada, forgive me, and come back to school, and I will tell them all what I did, and how wicked I was."

" Millicent, dear, I am very glad, very thankful. I wanted to make my last Communion tomorrow morning; will you be with me?"

" Her last?" and Millicent looked inquiringly at Harry.

He smiled a sweet grave smile as he answered, " Ada is going to rest, instead of to work."

The next morning, the Sacred Mysteries were celebrated in that chamber of death. All the girl most loved were with her then—Sister Agnes and Sister Kate, and above all Millicent.

Over that most solemn service we will draw a veil. When it was over the loving eyes were fixed upon those who stood around her, and then they closed for ever upon the things of earth.

That night Millicent Grey stood with Harry by the side of the bed, and laid a crown of lovely flowers upon the still breast. And he too placed an offering there—a faded chaplet; and he told the girl the story of his wreath, and she knelt in that still presence, and asked GOD to help her to be humble and true as Ada had been.

In the days that came afterwards that prayer was answered. There were those amongst the

poor and needy who could tell of the girl's deeds
of kindness and self-denial, of her care and
thought for others. And amongst her companions, those who had known her in the days
of her pride, there was a general feeling of as-
tonishment, as they noted the meek, humble
spirit, which always placed herself last,—thought
of herself as unworthy of all but the lowest
place.

LITTLE WAX-WORKS.

Twelfth Sunday after Trinity.

"Let all thy converse be sincere,
Thy conscience as the noon-day clear."

A GANG of unruly boys were shoving and pushing and screaming one hot August afternoon, trying to force their way into S. Lawrence's school, before the doors were open. Not that they wanted to get through the keyhole exactly, but there was something wrong with the lock, and one of them suggested that it would be good fun to force it asunder, and be sitting in their places by the time their teacher arrived.

They had not long been under training of any kind. It was only within the last few months that a few rough idle fellows had been gathered together, not by a Priest or a layman, but by a quiet gentle lady, who spent her life in good works, and who had a strange liking for boys of all ages, for the sake, it might have been, of two bright youths who had been the joy and sunshine of her widowed life, and who in one short week had been laid low by fever, and had gone, their mother humbly hoped, to where GOD giveth His beloved sleep.

After their death Mrs. Spencer had left her home, which had been in a little quiet country village, and had taken up her abode in the seaport town of S. Lawrence.

She felt that now she must live for others; that to bear the burdens and the sorrows of her poorer neighbours would be the only cure for the grief which had come into her life,—the only oil to be poured upon those surging waves of bitterness, which at one time had threatened to overwhelm her.

She had chosen S. Lawrence, because a friend of hers had lately been appointed to the living, and when she was fairly settled there, and had begun to work amongst the sick and the needy, she went to the Vicar one day and said, " I want some boys, please, I don't care how uncouth they are." And he had told her she might have the schoolroom on Sunday afternoons during the children's service, and do the best she could with some of the roughs who were always standing idly about the corners of the streets, and who obstinately refused to enter the Church.

She had done her best; somehow those great noisy fellows were getting more civilized. They liked Sunday afternoons, they said; they liked the gentle way in which Mrs. Spencer spoke to them, and the stories she told them, and sometimes of an evening they would steal into Church, not caring for any one to see them, and yet behaving in a quiet, reverent, orderly fashion, which astonished those who knew what they had been, only a few short months before.

But still they were a noisy unruly crew, always making a noise and disturbance if they could get a chance of it, and on the bright Sunday afternoon when our story begins, they were more than usually riotous. The heat which oppressed every one else, seemed not to have the smallest effect in quieting their exuberant spirits.

They succeeded in forcing open the door, and then one of them caught sight of a tall figure in a black dress coming down the street, and he announced to the others that Mrs. Spencer was coming, and so they took their places just with a little more pushing and shoving, and then they found that there was a stranger amongst them, a small fair boy, with blue eyes and light hair, and clothed, or rather *not* clothed, in ragged tattered garments. Arms and knees and feet were for the most part bare, and there was a look upon the lad's face that told of want and poverty of no common kind.

The other boys looked askance at him; for he had sat down amongst them quite calmly, as if he had as good a right to be there as they had; and when they stared at him rudely, he bore it unflinchingly, and seemed in no way abashed thereby.

"Who is he?" said one to the other.

"I've seen the chap somewhere before, but I don't quite know where."

"I can tell you," said John Jarvis, a big, good-natured fellow, "I can tell you who it is; it's Little Wax-works."

"Little Wax-works, Jack; what do you mean?"

"Why, the chap as stands at the door where the wax-works is showing, dressed up like a small Scotchman, a-taking of the money."

"Why, so it is. I say, Wax-works, what do you want here?"

The boy did not answer, and the question was repeated.

Still no reply, and there was a general cry of "Turn him out."

Then a faint tinge of colour rose to the pale cheek, and Little Wax-works held by both hands on to the form, thereby showing that he meant to resist the decree.

Two or three of the lads got up and went up to him ; but John Jarvis bade them keep their hands off the boy, and they knew that if they did not obey him it would be worse for them.

"Keep your hands off," he repeated, "he can come here if he likes ; I'm sure Mrs. Spencer would say so if we asked her."

"What would Mrs. Spencer say?" said a sweet gentle voice ; and the boys all got up to welcome their teacher.

"If you please, ma'am," said Jarvis, "we was a-talking of Little Wax-works,—him as is sitting there. Some of them said he ought to be turned out, but I said I was sure you would say if he liked to come he might."

"Of course he may," answered Mrs. Spencer, looking kindly at the ragged urchin ; "but what did you say his name was, Jarvis? I didn't quite catch it."

"I calls him Little Wax-works," answered Jarvis, laughing. And then he proceeded to explain the reason why he had bestowed this appellation upon the new comer.

All this time the subject of the discussion was sitting in the place he had chosen when he first came in; and Mrs. Spencer went up to him, and said,

"My boy, what is your name?"

"I ain't got ne'er a one."

"Not got a name? What do they call you at home?"

"I ain't got a home."

"When your father and mother, or your brothers and sisters want you, what do they say?"

"I ain't got ne'er a father or mother, or brothers or sisters."

Mrs. Spencer could not resist a smile, and there was a loud titter from the boys, which she knew it would be useless to try and suppress.

"Then I think I must call you by the name John has given you, 'Little Wax-works.'"

The boy grinned from ear to ear.

"Yes, that will do as well as anything else," he answered; "it's better than what *he* calls me."

"Who is *he* ?"

"Tom Butler."

"Please, ma'am, that's him that the wax-works belongs to," put in one of the boys *sotto voce.*

"Yes, some of them belongs to him," continued the stranger, waxing more confidential, "but some is only out on hire. Queen Elizabeth and Cardinal Wolsey ain't Tom's."

"Well, my man, I should like to hear all about the wax-works by-and-by, but I am afraid we must not talk any more now; only I think I should like to know what Tom Butler calls you."

"Donkey," responded the boy, amidst a shout of laughter; "he says I is one, so I'd best be called that, and I's obliged to answer him, or he would give me a whacking."

Mrs. Spencer was really interested in the poor little fellow; there was something in his face, something in the wistful glance of his blue eyes, that sent a thrill of compassion to the loving heart of the teacher.

"What brought you here to-day, my boy ?"

This time the lad fairly blushed, and then he said in a low voice,

"To see you."

"To see me? Why, what do you know about me?"

"I was a-standing at the door of the caravan yesterday, and I seed you pick up a little chap as had fallen down, and heard you speak ever so kind to him; and I axed a fellow where you lived, and he told me as you always comed here on Sundays; so thinks I, I'll go and see the lady to-morrow, and perhaps she'll speak kind to me."

The other lads did not laugh now; they were good-hearted fellows in the main, and thoughtless though they generally were, they could trace marks of suffering upon poor Little Wax-works' face; and it seemed hard that he should have to come there just to hear one kind word, as though that were his only chance of being thus addressed.

"Now, my boys," said Mrs. Spencer, "we really must begin our lesson. I am going to say a little to you to-day about the Collect, and I am not going to read you a story. Come, you need not look so disappointed; I want you all to come and have tea with me instead."

There was a general murmur of satisfaction at this announcement. Mrs. Spencer had had , one tea-party before, and it must be confessed the charm of sitting in her cheerful room, and partaking of rich plum cake, somewhat counterbalanced the boys' regret at not hearing a story.

"Well, my boys, on this Twelfth Sunday after Trinity, we confess to GOD that He 'is always more ready to hear than we are to pray, and is wont to give us more than we either desire or deserve.'

"You know this is quite true; you know that GOD is always bending His ear to earth, to listen to what we have to say to Him; and oh, how it must grieve Him when some of us refuse to speak, refuse to ask Him for what we want, refuse to tell Him our sorrows and our troubles.

"If you loved any one very much indeed, and you wanted to show how dear they were to you, would you not go to that person and ask what you could do for him, how you could help him?"

"Yes, ma'am," answered the boys.

"Well, if he refused your help, if he would not listen to your words of affection, if he obstinately refused to speak to you, what would happen, what would you do?"

"We should be angry," said one of the lads.

"We should leave him to himself," answered another.

"Yes, very probably many of us would; our weak erring human affection could not bear the slight; would not be long-suffering and patient enough to stand it—but GOD never leaves us to ourselves; He is grieved at our want of trust in Him, but He does not turn away from us, He is always bidding us speak to Him, and pray to Him; there is not one minute through all the long day, nor through all the dark dreary night, that He is not bending over us in love; ready, anxious to hear the faintest word that we say to Him.

"And then He always gives us more than we either desire or deserve—to desire is to wish, to want, and the things that GOD will give us, if we ask Him, are so wonderful and so beautiful, even the joys and glories of heaven, that our poor wishes cannot rise so high—we cannot realize what our happiness will be if we love our FATHER in heaven, and pray to Him as He bids us do.

"And we deserve nothing from Him; we are always sinning, always doing wrong, always offending Him, and yet in His mercy and His love JESUS came down from heaven to earth, to obtain for us those good things to which we could have no claim unless He had died for us.

"The Collect goes on to say: 'Pour down upon us the abundance of Thy mercy, forgiving us those things of which our conscience is afraid, and giving us those good things which we are not worthy to ask, but through the merits and mediation of JESUS CHRIST, Thy SON, our LORD.'

"Do you know what your conscience is, my boys?"

"Please, ma'am, ain't it that as is inside us, and tells us when we have done wrong?" answered John Jarvis.

"Quite right, John; and now what are those things of which our conscience is afraid?"

"Wrong things."

"Yes, wrong things; not those great glaring open sins of ours, which every one sees, and for which we are punished here on earth—at least of course we must be afraid of these sins, and of GOD's anger, but I think the Collect to-day speaks to us of secret sins—of sins known only to ourselves and to GOD, but which we remember with sorrow and fear afterwards.

"Have you never had such a feeling in your hearts, boys? have you never done a wrong thing, and the thought of that wrong thing has come back to you very often, and made you very unhappy.   Your conscience has been afraid ·of it.

"Some of you even now can think of such things.   Will you, when you are in Church this evening, and I hope all of you will go to Church, ask GOD to forgive you these sins, and to give you those good things which you are not worthy to ask, save through the merits and mediation of JESUS CHRIST our LORD.

"You were quite right, John, when you said that conscience is that that is inside us which tells us when we have done wrong—but we should indeed be unhappy, we should indeed have very little hope, unless there was a help given us to guide our conscience aright.   Do you know what that help is ?"

"The HOLY SPIRIT, that was given us when we were baptised."

"Yes, the HOLY SPIRIT it is, that is our only help and strength ; when our conscience is afraid, when we feel that GOD is angry with us because of our sins, then we must ask the HOLY GHOST to be in our hearts and to make us sorry, and bring us back to the right way.

"You can, all of you, do this ; you have all now, thank GOD, been made GOD's own children in Holy Baptism ; most of you, I hope, before very long will receive the great blessing of Confirmation. I have talked to you about this and about the Blessed Sacrament before, and I will do so again, but not to-day; I have kept you longer than I intended as it is, and I think our tea must be quite ready. I only want to say one word more to you; will you try and keep from those things of which your conscience is afraid? will you, when temptation comes to you, pause for an instant, and ask GOD the HOLY GHOST to show you what is right for JESUS CHRIST'S sake?"

"Yes, ma'am, we will try," came from several of the boys; and Mrs. Spencer knew they would, for, for all their rough ways, she felt that they were trying to be good, and that the work she had undertaken in love, was bringing many blessings with it.

She went up to Little Wax-works kindly. "You will come and have some tea at my house, won't you, my boy?"

"They says I can't; that my clothes is too bad."

"Who says so?"

"Them chaps," answered the poor little fellow, pointing to two or three boys who were standing apart, engaged in an apparently very animated discussion; "him as has the blue tie, and the red pin, was the one who said the most about it; and you see, ma'am, Tom won't allow me to wear my Highland suit a Sundays, he says it's too good when there's nothing to do."

"Well, perhaps you could hardly come here in your Highland suit, so it is just as well as it is, but I don't think they really meant that you must not come to my house to tea; anyhow, if I say you are to, I am sure no one will say a word against it."

So Little Wax-works followed in the stream, and John Jarvis took him under his especial protection, and the poor little pale face was really lit up with a new joy as the boy sat in the pretty cheerful room, and ate his bread and butter, and cake, and drank the nice sweet tea with as hearty good will as any of his companions.

When the meal was over Mrs. Spencer told the boys to go for a walk, begging them however to be sure to get back in time for Evensong.

"I hope he ain't coming with us," said Robert Anson, the owner of the blue tie and red pin before alluded to, darting a somewhat contemptuous glance at "Little Wax-works."

Mrs. Spencer heard the speech, and hastened to re-assure Robert on this point. Kind and loving though she was, she quite understood the weaknesses and foibles of those around her, and truth to tell, she was hardly astonished at the boy, not particularly caring to walk out on Sunday in company with the ragged little stranger; it was *boylike*, she thought, although some strait-laced folks might have said, not quite *Christian-like*, but Rome was not built in a day, and the lads of Mrs. Spencer's class were being built up bit by bit in Christian faith and gentleness, and meekness.

"Will you stay at home with me, my man, and tell me something about the wax-works?"

And the poor boy was only too happy to be allowed to spend an hour with his new friend.

He took a long time telling his story; we have not space in this little tale to tell all the conversation that passed between him and Mrs. Spencer as they sat side by side in the garden on that sweet August evening, but in as few words as we can we will give you a summary of Little Wax-works' tale.

He did not know who his father and mother were; he never remembered to have known them; all his life he had lived with Tom Butler, and had moved about from place to place with the caravan; he had been beaten, and starved, and kicked, and nobody had ever said a kind word to him for ever so long, never since Tom Butler's girl, Annie, died, and went away to heaven.

She had taught the boy to read, and she had given him her Bible,—the Bible that had been her mother's,—and sometimes she had told him about GOD and about JESUS, and the Angels, but she had forgotten most of what she had learned, and he was not allowed to be with her very much before she went away.

"What used she to call you, my boy?" asked Mrs. Spencer.

"Donkey," was the answer; "it comed natural like to her, she didn't say it like Tom says it, she used to say it quite gentle like, more like you speaks; she told me once that I had never been christened. Mother died the day I was born, and father was gône afore that; he had a share in the wax-works, he had, and Tom ought to give me some money, but he never will, and I hates him."

Altogether it was a touching little story, full of such intense loneliness and desolation, and through it all Mrs. Spencer could detect the

yearning for some one to love him, the longing
for a kind word, which had brought little Wax-
works to S. Lawrence's school on that Sunday
afternoon.

Very kindly she spoke to the poor boy, trying to tell him of all GOD's goodness, and speaking to him of that grace of Baptism of which he
had never been made a partaker.

It was settled between them that she should
go to the caravan the very next day, and see
Tom Butler.

"He ain't always very civil, ma'am, but he's
sure to be civil to you, because you're such a
grand lady, and you speaks so nice, and Queen
Elizabeth is worth seeing, ma'am, she's beautiful, she is, and so is the sleeping hinfant that's
breathing, and looking all the world as if she
was alive."

"You will come to Church with me, my boy,
won't you?"

"I should like to, ma'am, I heard the music
outside last Sunday, and it was just beautiful, it
was, but Tom would whack me if I wasn't home
at seven o'clock, and I can't bear another whacking, my back is sore enough now."

He was going away, and then he turned back
and stood shyly before Mrs. Spencer.

"I often does wrong things.; I's often afeard that GOD will be angry with me; will it be better when you've took me to Church and had me christened?"

And his friend spoke to him again of all the help that would come with the great grace.

The next day Mrs. Spencer found her way to the caravan; she hardly recognised little Wax-works in his Highland. attire, but he smiled brightly as she spoke to him, and he ushered her into Tom Butler's presence with as much ceremony as though she had been the queen.

The proprietor of the show, an ill-looking fellow, was highly gratified at the visit, particularly as Mrs. Spencer at once took several tickets for the entertainment; and when she spoke of the boy, and asked if he might be allowed to come to her for an hour every morning before the exhibition opened, he placed no obstacle in the way of the plan, and insisted upon displaying to her the beauties of his establishment.

So it was all settled; they were to stay at S. Lawrence a whole month, Little Wax-works said, and early every morning the boy found his way either to Mrs. Spencer's house or to the Vicarage, and learned what a solemn vow, promise, and profession that was which he was about to take upon himself.

Every Sunday too he appeared at the class. Mrs. Spencer had given him a decent suit of clothes, and the other boys, John Jarvis at their head, pronounced him a "plucky little fellow," and made a kind of pet and plaything of him.

He used to go to Church whenever he could, and he loved the music better than anything else on earth, and once he asked John if there would be music like that in Heaven.

" Ever so much better," had been John's answer, and afterwards he remembered how the blue eyes had been lifted to the cloudless summer sky, and how Little Wax-works had said, " I should like to go there ; I know I don't deserve it, because of what Mrs. Spencer said the first Sunday as ever I comed to the school; but because Jesus died for me, perhaps He'll take me there before very long."

" I shouldn't wonder if He did, Little Wax-works," was the answer, and John wondered why he felt so " choky-like" as he looked into the little pale thin face.

One soft September evening Little Wax-works went to Church, and stood at the Holy Font, and was made a member of CHRIST, a child of GOD, and an inheritor of the Kingdom of Heaven.

They called the boy Cyprian, for it was on the Feast of the holy Archbishop and Martyr that the great Gift of the HOLY GHOST came to the lonely boy.

He was very still and quiet, and a smile of joy was on his face when all was over, and the Spirit's seal was set upon his brow.

"We are going away soon," he said to Mrs. Spencer, "but I don't mind it now; I shall be sorry to leave you and the Vicar and John, but the HOLY SPIRIT will be with me to help me to keep from wrong things; and perhaps if I'm good GOD will give me more than I deserve, and take me away."

And Mrs. Spencer too had the same choky feeling in her throat as John Jarvis had had, as she listened to Cyprian's words.

A week passed away, and it was announced on a huge placard outside the caravan that it was positively the last day of the gorgeous display of wax-works, unrivalled in all England, superior even to Madame Tussaud herself.

Almost every one in S. Lawrence had seen

the show, and Cyprian stood at the door beating a drum, and shouting to the people to come in, because this was their last chance.

Nobody responded to the invitation, and Tom Butler sat alone with the wax figures, with a scowl of mingled anger and despair upon his low brow.

Late that night he called the boy to him. "Donkey," he said, "I'm ruined; there's but one hope for us; you know the place is insured, I'm going out for a bit; I wants some rubbishy papers burned, they're along of that straw in the corner; when I'm gone put a match to them, and then run off as fast as you can."

The boy was sharp enough to understand what this meant,—that the caravan and its contents were to be burned, and that he was required to aid and abet the fraud.

"I can't do it," he said, "indeed I can't,— I mustn't."

"Mustn't,—who says that? who dares to tell you not to do as I bids you?"

"My conscience," answered the boy boldly; "I mustn't do things I knows is wrong, or GOD will not let me go and live with Him when I dies."

There was a muttered exclamation, a fierce

oath, and a heavy blow fell on Cyprian's head.
The boy reeled and fell senseless to the ground.

Another half-hour and the caravan was in
flames; an alarm was given by a passer-by, and
the police rescued a little scorched burnt figure
from the fire.

" Take him to the lady's house, it's the
nearest," and so he was carried to Mrs. Spencer's, and he lay there for more than a week
suffering untold agony.

They could make nothing of his incoherent
ravings; he was always talking of the straw and
the matches, and saying, " My conscience was
afraid, I could not do it; I have often done
wrong things, but GOD is very good, and JESUS
died for me."

At the last there came relief from suffering,
and with it all the clearness returned to the
boy's mind. Then he told his story; and the
Vicar said to Mrs. Spencer, "We little thought
one short week ago how worthy our little Cyprian
would be of his Martyr's name,—how he would
die for conscience' sake."

He asked to see John Jarvis, and he bade
him good-bye, and sent his love to the others.
"Give them Little Wax-works' love," he said,
"and say that GOD has given him more than he

deserves;" and he asked Mrs. Spencer to kiss him, and then he fell asleep.

A plain stone cross bears his name, "Cyprian," and the date of his death, and the words, " Suffered for conscience' sake;" and on summer evenings the boys of Mrs. Spencer's class, many of whom have been confirmed and are communicants, now lay wreaths of flowers there and talk of " Little Wax-works."

Tom Butler was never heard of again after that September night, when Queen Elizabeth and Cardinal Wolsey, and all the other celebrities perished in the flames.

It is a simple story, this story of Little Wax-works, but it is a true one, told to the writer by one who knew and loved the little ignorant boy who gave up his life so bravely for conscience' sake. Dear children, trials come to you as they did to him; it may be that very often you are tempted to do what you know to be wrong, that the sweet White Dove given to you at your Baptism is telling you in soft loving accents that you are grieving Him because you wilfully close your eyes to what is right, because you will not heed the voice of conscience. Will you ask GOD to pour down upon you the abundance of His mercy, and to forgive you those sins of which your conscience is afraid, for JESUS CHRIST'S sake?

GO AND DO THOU LIKEWISE.

"Give and forgive, do good and love,
By soft endearments in kind strife,
Lightening the load of daily life."

EVERY one in Brambleton knew what every one else did; every one could tell at what hour every one dined and drank tea, and had their supper. Some went a little further, and could speak both of the quality and quantity of food of which their neighbours partook.

"We are a band of brothers and sisters," one old lady had said, describing the intimate terms on which the Brambletonians lived with each other, "but I don't think I like it," she added, "I think I should like a little less discussion about my private affairs; but it's all kindly meant, I know, and I must bear it."

V.   K

This is only by way of preface to show you what kind of place Brambleton was. I dare say many of you can quite imagine it; a small country town with a market-place, and a Guildhall, and a Mechanics' Institute, and a few shops, and some old red brick houses, and nothing else worthy of note about it, that is to say, in a secular way; but Brambleton had something of which it was justly proud, a beautiful old Church, which had once belonged to an Abbey, and although no trace of the other part of the building was to be found, (all had been swept away by the ruthless hands of our Puritan ancestors,) GOD'S House still stood in all its glory, telling of the faith and piety of those holy ones of old, who had raised that noble pile to their Master's honour.

Brambleton lay deep down in a valley, but the Church stood at the top of a hill just above the town; wherever you walked you could see the stately tower, and the carved buttresses, and the ivy-covered windows,—all seemed to speak of hope and of peace, to beckon wayfarers up the steep ascent to where they should find rest unto their souls.

One Saturday night towards the middle of September a lad was wending his way to the

House of Prayer. He was a nice-looking boy, tall, and slight, and active, but his face wore an expression of sadness unusual in one so young, and as he walked along his head was bent and his eyes were fixed upon the ground, as though he would avoid the notice of the few people who were going to their homes from their day's work.

It was a glorious evening, and yet there was something of sadness in it; there had been a heavy gale a few hours before, although all was now so calm and still and peaceful, and the yellow leaves were lying thick upon the ground, and the trees had become strangely bare since that same hour on the previous day. There was a foreshadowing of winter gloom coming, as it were, to take away the last remnant of summer gladness.

The boy of whom we have spoken, and whose name was Arthur Longmore, kicked away the leaves somewhat impatiently as he strode along, and then as he reached the churchyard gate he looked down the hill upon the little town lying there in the fast-gathering darkness, and he sighed a deep-drawn sigh, and muttered,

"They all know it now, I suppose, they are all talking about it now; I dare say some of

them are sorry, I am sure they are; but they'll
be hard upon us in our disgrace if I know anything of them."

There was bitterness in the tone and a look
upon the boyish face that told of wounded pride,
that made the sorrow, whatever may have been
its cause, harder to bear even than it would
otherwise have been.

He opened the Church door and went in;
reverently he knelt at the chancel steps, and
asked GOD to help him and all he loved in the
trial that had come upon them on that September day.

He was disturbed at last by the clanking of
feet upon the stone pavement; he knew it was
Old Joe the verger come to shut up the Church
for the night. Lingeringly and regretfully he
rose from his knees; it was all so peaceful there,
neither sin nor sorrow seemed to have any place
in GOD's own House, as the moonbeams fell so
softly through the painted windows, and aisle
and nave and pillar were lit up with their sweet
mellow light.

Old Joe was a kind of institution in Brambleton; men who were grey-headed now had never
remembered him different to what he was then;
he had been Old Joe when they were little boys,

and he did not appear to have grown a day
older since that time.

He hobbled up the nave now, and muttered
to himself that he must turn whoever was there
out; it was past closing time as it was, and he
always liked to be early on Saturday nights.

But when he saw Arthur Longmore's slight
form, a look of great pity and compassion came
upon the rugged old face.

"Poor lad," he said to himself, "poor lad, I
don't mind waiting five minutes or so; I dare
say it's a comfort to him to be here; I know
I've found it the very greatest as could come to
me many and many a time when I've been in
trouble."

And Joe sat down upon a seat, and resigned
himself to circumstances. His patience was not
long taxed; Arthur, as we have seen, had already risen from his knees, and was only standing to gaze at the glorious stained glass of the
east window as the moon passed behind it, and
brought out the scene of the Crucifixion in such
a strange, mysterious, marvellous way.

"I never saw it look like that in the sunshine,"
mused the boy, "never half so solemn or so
beautiful."

Ay, surely, it is in the hours of darkness and

of gloom that the story of ineffable love comes
to us with a new beauty and a new power, and
the beams of mercy light it up with rays of light
that were not there in the brightness and glory
of the mid-day sun.

The old man rose as the lad walked down
the nave; the bitterness all gone from his young
face, only an expression of patient sorrow left
there.

Old Joe held out his rough hand.

"Master Arthur, I'm so sorry; he was always
so kind to me, sir, and I can't say a word against
him now; I was saying to my old missis afore
I comed out, 'I can't hit a man when he's
down,' so if I can do anything for you or your
good mother, I'll do it, and only be too proud;
anyhow," and he lowered his voice to a whisper,
"anyhow, sir, I'll pray for you, and GOD hears
the prayers of the poorest and the humblest of
His creatures."

Arthur grasped the proffered hand warmly;
he could not speak, his heart, poor fellow, was
too full for words; he muttered an almost unin-
telligible "Thank you, Joe," and then he passed
out again into the chill autumn air.

Very quickly he ran down the hill, and soon
reached his home,—that home which once had

been so bright and cheery,—but upon which a
nameless shadow had hung for many months;
and the night before our story begins the nameless shadow, the cloud which had been no bigger
than a man's hand, had burst into a great
storm.

Arthur Longmore's father was a lawyer, that
is to say, he had been brought up to the study
of the law; but another solicitor named Bransdon had settled in Brambleton and carried all
before him. Mr. Longmore found it very hard
to make both ends meet, and thankfully accepted the Duke of Martindale's offer to become
his steward and agent.

He had held the post now for some years,
apparently to the satisfaction of his employer,
and evidently very much to his own benefit.
He had lived in a very small house when he
first came to Brambleton, but very soon after
he received his new appointment he had removed to a great red brick mansion at the entrance of the town, and there he lived, and
there he kept his horses and carriages, and
hunters, and folks began to wonder where he
got his money, and at last there were ugly rumours afloat as to how it all came into his possession. The last people to hear these rumours

were his gentle little wife, and his young son and daughter.

Brambleton might talk to its heart's content, and of course Brambleton did talk, but it could hardly tell its suspicions to Mr. Longmore's own belongings, and so things went on, and those who were really most interested in the gossip heard nothing at all about it.

Mrs. Longmore could not tell why it was that suddenly the sunshine had seemed to go out of her hitherto happy life. Arthur and Edith could not account for the difference in their father's manner both to themselves and to their mother.

There was a time when all their pleasures and amusements had been his delight; when to sit with their parents of an evening and to talk of all they had done at school during the day had been considered their right and their privilege.

But lately this had not been. Mr. Longmore was always shut up in the library bending over dusky old ledgers and quires of ruled paper, and even Edith, who was his especial darling, was often ordered roughly away, if she dared to disturb his solitude.

Mrs. Longmore had always been an invalid,

and it had been her husband's way to keep the details of his money affairs from her. She had sometimes tried to talk to him about them, but he had always evaded the subject; he gave her a certain sum for housekeeping, which she used most carefully, and with this she was obliged to be satisfied.

On that September day of which we are writing the cloud burst. Mr. Longmore had been away from home a week, and he had written to his wife a loving, humble, penitent letter, telling her of his sin; he had speculated with money that was not his own; the speculation had failed, and he was a ruined man. The Duke he knew would be furious; he was a hot-tempered but most good-hearted man; and there was no hope for the faithless steward but in flight. Every one in Brambleton would know of his disgrace that day, he said; bills would be presented at the bank, and dishonoured, and probably before night a warrant for his apprehension would be out. He begged his wife not to seek to follow him; he gave no clue to whither he was going; her small jointure of a hundred a year was safe, he said; he had not tampered with that.

The weak delicate fragile little woman, whom

every one had hitherto looked upon as somewhat of a nonentity, braced herself up now for
her children's sake; she was strong in the hour
of trial—strong in a strength that was not her
own. After the first bitterness of grief had passed,
she thought of her boy and girl; she told them
the truth; it was useless to seek to hide it from
them, and perhaps the hardest thing she had to
bear was the look that came upon Arthur's face
as he said,

"Won't Bransdon be triumphant, won't he
crow over us!"

"We must not think of such things now, my
darling; we must try and be very humble and
very patient; others must do as they please;
we have only to think of ourselves, and perhaps,
oh, Arthur," and all a woman's loving tenderness
was in the tearful eyes, "perhaps, oh, Arthur, if
we bear our trouble bravely, people will speak
less unkindly of him."

"They dare not speak against him," was the
reply; "he never harmed any one—he was
always good to every one."

"To every one but himself," was the gentle
answer; "it was his good-nature and hospitality
that—that—I cannot speak of it—but, Arthur,
we must face it out; he has done wrong. Oh,

GOD, be merciful to me, for having to say it of him,—and we must bear the penalty."

"We cannot stay here—we must not."

"I think we must, my boy; the small house in High Street is, you know, vacant, and not likely to let; it belongs to me, we must go and live in it; it will save our rent."

It was after this conversation that poor Arthur had gone to the Church he had loved ever since he was a little boy, and there he had found the rest and peace he sought.

When he entered the room where his mother and his young sister sat he went up and kissed them both, and they knew where he had been, even before he told them of Old Joe's kind words.

Let us have a glimpse at another home in Brambleton on that September night. A gentleman and a lady, and a youth, apparently about the same age as Arthur Longmore, are sitting in a spacious dining-room over their dessert.

"I tell you I will not have it, Donald; I forbid you to speak to the fellow again."

"Father, he has been my friend for so long."

"I am aware of that, but it does not alter the

case now; a man of my position," (for it was
Mr. Bransdon the prosperous lawyer who was
speaking,) "cannot afford to allow his son to
mix himself up with a set of swindlers."

Donald winced; he and Arthur had played
together since they were two years old; they
had gone to Miss Buckram's morning class for
small boys and girls, and had been instructed
by that worthy lady in reading, writing, and
arithmetic, and in the rudiments of Latin; and
on the same day they had been entered as
pupils at Brambleton Grammar School, and now
they were in the first class of that flourishing
academy, and they were looking forward to the
not far distant day when they should leave good
old Doctor Grinder's care, and enter into business of some kind.

Donald Bransdon had a great many faults;
but by nature he was loving and generous, and
never in all his hitherto bright young life had
he felt as he felt that evening when his father
bade him cut Arthur Longmore.

"I shall tell him my wishes myself," continued
the stern lawyer; "you might lack courage to
do it; there shall be no excuse of this kind."

"Mother," said poor Donald, "do ask if I
may speak to him just sometimes. I know it

will make his trouble all the harder if I turn away from him now."

Mrs. Bransdon was the last person likely to aid her son in this matter; she was a prejudiced narrow-minded woman, and she drew herself up now and looked at the boy with a cold hard expression in her grey eyes.

"Your father is perfectly right, Donald; I certainly cannot ask him to let you disgrace yourself."

And all poor Donald could do was to run away from the table, and go up to his own room, and throw himself on the bed and sob as though his heart would break. Don't think him unmanly because he let his grief have way; there was no harm in that, only it would have been better if he had done as Arthur did, and asked GOD to help him in the really heavy trial that had come to him. The truth was, that Donald's will was a very undisciplined one, and he could not bear that any one should cross it. He chafed and rebelled against things instead of trying to be patient and to bear them.

Very early the next morning Arthur and his mother, and sisters, knelt at the altar of GOD, and sought for strength in the heavy sorrow which had come to them.

There were those in Brambleton who wondered that they could "show themselves so soon," and who didn't think it "looked well ;" but Old Joe went home and said to his missis, (as he always called her,) "I was awful sorry for them yesterday, poor things, and so I is to-day, but somehow some of the sorrow went away, as I seed them a-kneeling there this morning, for I felt as they was safe, beneath the Everlasting Arms." And surely Brambleton was wrong, and Old Joe was right.

It was the strength that Arthur received there that made him able to bear what happened only half an hour afterwards ; when as he was on his way to the Post Office to see if there were any letters (for there was no Sunday delivery in the little country town,) Mr. Bransdon and Donald passed him, and the father drew his son to the other side of the street.

"Oh, Donald," was all the poor fellow murmured, "I never expected this," but not one thought of anger or of hatred was in Arthur's heart on that bright Sunday morning as he pursued his sorrowful way to the Post Office.

There *was* a letter from his father bearing a foreign post mark, and when Arthur reached home he kept his sorrow to himself, and listened eagerly to the news his mother had to tell.

Mr. Longmore wrote a short hurried scrawl. " I will not rest until I have paid the Duke the money I have wronged him of," he said. And Arthur knelt by his mother's couch, and as she looked into his face it seemed to her as though a strange new strength had come upon the boyish features in those few hours of trial.

" Mother, in Church this morning, I too vowed that I would make restitution to the Duke— whatever the cost to myself."

Mrs. Longmore drew her boy more closely to her and kissed him fondly. And Edith, sitting apart and hearing the words, thought as she had often thought before that there was no one in all the world half so good, or half as noble, as Arthur.

Mrs. Longmore was too ill to go to Church again that morning, and Edith stayed to take care of her mother; Arthur went alone; it was a struggle to face the crowd, but he knew that sooner or later it must be done; and the people were very kind on the whole, and many a hat was doffed as the boy walked quickly up the hill, evidently seeking to avoid notice.

Again help came to him, as he knelt before

the Blessed Sacrament, and when service was
over, he waited for the Vicar, whom he had seen
the day before, and who had shown himself to
the Longmores the true friend he always was to
any one in trouble.

"Will you lend me a book, please, sir?
Edith always likes me to read to her during the
afternoon, and I don't think we shall go for a
walk to-day."

"Yes, my boy, take this; I think you will
like the part about to-day's Gospel, the parable
of the Good Samaritan. I think, Arthur, it may
be a help to you just now."

Then Arthur told the good Priest what was in
his mind, and asked him to help him to find
something to do, so that he might earn money
enough to pay the Duke the hundreds of which
he had been defrauded.

"GOD bless and help you, my boy," was the
answer; "I will do my best for you."

That afternoon Arthur read to his mother and
Edith, out of the book the Vicar had lent him,
the explanation of the parable of the Good Samaritan, which was the Gospel for that Sunday,
the Thirteenth after Trinity.

"A certain lawyer stood up and tempted our
Blessed LORD; that is, tried to make Him say

something which would show His ignorance of the law.

" ' Master, what shall I do to inherit eternal life ?'

" Then JESUS asked him what the command of the law was ; and the lawyer answered, ' Thou shalt love the LORD thy GOD with all thy heart, and with all thy soul, and with all thy strength, and thy neighbour as thyself.'

" Then again came the question, ' Who is my neighbour ?'

" And for answer, JESUS speaks that most beautiful parable which is so familiar to us all.

" There is a beautiful mystical meaning in the story, which we must just glance at. The certain man who went down from Jerusalem to Jericho is a type of Adam, and of ourselves, the children of Adam ; and he *went down* from Jerusalem, the vision of peace, to Jericho. And Jericho here is the type of sin. He fell among thieves, who take from him his innocence, and despoil him of his original righteousness, leaving him covered with wounds, and powerless to rise from his fallen state.

" The poor wounded man lay all helpless by the road-side. A Priest and a Levite passed by him, but they did not help him, for as has

been well said, they were unable to help, unable
to save, for they too were wounded in the
wounded man.   Then came the Good Samaritan, and when He saw ˙him He had compassion on him, and bound up his wounds, pouring
therein oil and wine.   The Good Samaritan is
the SAVIOUR of the world, He Who was despised
and rejected of men.

"Then He sets the poor sufferer on His own
beast, and walks by his side as a servant, and
takes him to the inn, which is the Church, and
leaves him there in safe keeping, until He shall
come again to judge both the quick and the
dead.

"But before He departed, i.e., before He ascended into heaven, He took two pence, and
gave them to the Host, the two pence bearing
the image of the King, being those two Sacra-
ments ordained by CHRIST Himself as the
nourishment of Christian souls in their journey
through life.

"This is the mystical meaning of the parable
of the Good Samaritan; the literal meaning is
plain enough.   We too are to learn to show
mercy, not by looking on quietly at the troubles
and sorrows that are sent to our neighbours,
even although those troubles may be of their

own making. We are to show special mercy when a man is, so to speak, *down.* We are neither to show prejudice, nor contempt, nor hatred; we are to be as our own most blessed LORD was, merciful to *all,*—in a word, let us take as our rule of life the lesson taught us by the Good Samaritan,—let us take as our maxim the words of the Master as our sure, our only passport to eternal life, ' Go and do thou likewise.' "

" My boy," said Mrs. Longmore, when Arthur ceased reading, " shall we ask GOD to help us to-day, of all days, to bear no malice nor hatred in our hearts ?"

Another week, and the mother and daughter were settled in the little house in High Street, and Arthur had gone to an office in London to a friend of the Vicar's, to try and earn money enough to pay his father's just debts.

He knew it would take a long time to do this —he knew that it might be his life's work ; but he never flinched or wavered from his determination.   He went steadily on in the strength of his right purpose, and GOD was with the lad; and Old Joe had said rightly when he told his missis, that he knew that those sorrowing ones were safe beneath the Everlasting Arms.

In the quiet of the early morning, Arthur kneeling in a beautiful Church—one of the many to be found in London now, where the Holy Sacrifice is offered daily—found rest and refreshment for his soul. And the loving mother and sister at home prayed for their darling who was so far away.

Mr. Longmore died within one short year of his disgrace; and his wife and his children mourned for him as sorrowfully as though this trouble had never come upon them through his fault.

And then they went back to their daily lives Arthur to his office work, Mrs. Longmore to her embroidery, Edith to her painting, to try as best they could by earnest self-denial, to repair ever so little of the wrong he had done.

Ten years had passed away since that September day on which our story begins. Arthur had received a telegram, and had journeyed to Brambleton with all haste. The words of the message had been, "Good news; come home at once." And the good news was that an old cousin, whom none of them had ever seen, scarcely even heard of, was dead, and had left them all her money.

And they paid those long-standing debts, and still there was enough left for them to live upon comfortably.

One night Arthur stood in the Vicar's study, a flush on his brow, a glad light in his eye.

"I have brought this, sir. You have wanted a Mission Chapel on Thornton Heath for a long time—I saved it in London. I do not want it for that purpose now; oh, sir, might it go to help build the Chapel?"

And the Vicar's eyes filled with tears, as he saw a bank note for a thousand pounds, and knew at what a cost of self-denial the money must have been saved.

"It shall be begun at once, Arthur; I will have the plans drawn out next week."

The day after another panic had fallen upon the little town : Mr. Bransdon had failed, through no fault of his own, and he and his wife and son were penniless.

Arthur met Donald in the street. He had not spoken to him since that September morning ten years ago, but now he went up to him, and took his hand, and said,

"Donald, I wish I could help you."

"Thanks," and there was something of haughtiness in the tone, "no one can do that; we hoped we might have got a thousand pounds and that would have helped us just to pay ou immediate household debts, and to turn round but of course no one will trust us; and my mo ther is very ill."

"Poor Donald;" and Arthur went into the Church, and asked GOD to help him to a grea sacrifice.

Some strangers were looking about the Holy Building, and he knelt in a far away corner just beneath a small painted window, which re presented the Good Samaritan binding up the poor man's wounds. It seemed as though ar Angel's voice spoke to Arthur then, "Go anc do thou likewise."

He went to the Vicar and told his tale. Wha that tale was we must not seek to inquire; bu the Chapel on Thornton Heath is not built yet although there is a rumour that it will be shortly. And Arthur Longmore, having passec through his college course, is working hard as a Curate in an east end London parish, and hi mother and Edith live with him.

Donald is a frequent visitor at their house His father and mother are located in a little suburban cottage, and a change has come over those once hard hearts.

"Arthur, there is one thing I should like to know," said Donald, one day; "but I suppose I never shall—who could have sent us that thousand pounds? We pray for the unknown donor every day, and ask GOD to bless him; but I should like to thank him, to let him know all the good it did."

And Arthur turned away to hide his confusion, and then he said,

"I don't suppose he wants any thanks; your prayers will do him more good than your thanks could ever do."

"Be brave, my brother!
Fight the good fight of faith
   With weapons proved and true ;
Be faithful and unshrinking to the death,
   Thy GOD will bear thee through.
The strife is terrible,
   Yet 'tis not, 'tis not long ;
The foe is not invincible,
   Though fierce and strong.

"Be brave, my brother !
The recompense is great,
   The kingdom bright and fair ;
Beyond the glory of all earthly state
   Shall be the glory there.

Grudge not the heavy cost,
  Faint not at labour here,
'Tis but a life-time at the most,
  The day of rest is near.

  "Be brave, my brother !
He whom Thou servest slights
  Not even His weakest one ;
No deed though poor shall be forgot,
  However feebly done.
The prayer, the wish, the thought,
  The faintly spoken word,
The plan that seemed to come to nought,
  Each has its own reward !

  "Be brave, my brother !
Enlarge thy heart and soul,
  Spread out thy free glad love ;
Encompass earth, embrace the sea,
  As does that sky above.
Let no man see thee stand
  In slothful idleness,
As if there were no work for thee
  In such a wilderness.

  "Be brave, my brother !
Stint not the liberal hand,
  Give in the joy of love ;
So shall thy crown be bright, and great
  Thy recompense above.
Reward, not like the deed,—
  That poor weak deed of thine,—
But like the GOD Himself Who gives,
  Eternal and Divine."

BILL'S SISTER.

Fourteenth Sunday after Trinity.

"I long to be like JESUS,
  Meek, loving, lowly, mild,
I long to be like JESUS,
  The FATHER'S Holy Child."

"I TELL you I hate you, and I shall hate you always, not because of what you've done to me,—I don't mind that,—but you've struck my Bill, my little brother, and I won't stand it; and wait till the first time I gets a chance, and won't I give it you, that's all."

It was a girl who spoke, holding in her arms a little pale boy, who appeared at least some ten years her junior, for fourteen or fifteen summers must have passed over her head, and Bill could not have been more than three or four; indeed at a first glance the poor little emaciated

v.   L

face hardly looked as if it belonged to any one but a mere baby; but then you saw the length of limb, the thin legs hanging helplessly down, and the idea of babyhood went out of your head, and in its place came the sad thought of suffering childhood.

For we like to think that a child's life is bright, and gay, and happy; we like to hear the sound of little footsteps on the stairs, and the echo of blithe young voices comes to us with a ring of pleasure, which, unlike most of our earthly pleasures, has not a shadow of pain mixed up with it; and because of this we learn to look upon all pain in childhood as out of place, and to our poor weak human nature there seems something in it that is almost incongruous,—we forget that all children's sufferings have been blessed and sanctified by the Holy Sinless Child; we forget that on the first Festival of the Circumcision a cry went forth from the baby lips, when the first drop of His most Precious Blood was shed, which made all childish grief and pain sacred in the eyes of the Eternal FATHER for evermore. We forget that the suffering little ones have their own place in the loving Heart of their LORD, and He Who loveth those whom He chasteneth, will give them their reward when they lay down their little lives and go to the far off country where there is no more pain.

"Please don't, Patty," said the pleading voice of poor Bill; "please don't, Patty, indeed, indeed she did not hurt me much."

"She had no business to touch you, my precious darling," said the enraged Patty, "she's a bad, wicked girl, she is, and I'll be one with her yet."

And poor Bill hung his little head, and began to cry piteously.

Angry though she was there was something touching in the way in which the girl tried to soothe her charge; there was such a look of love in her dark eyes, as she bade him take comfort, and she would buy him a great big cake, that it was impossible to help feeling interested in her, in spite of her rage and her threats of vengeance.

The story of those two, of that elder sister and that little crippled brother, was very very sad. They had never known any other home but this great city of London; they had never been out of the precincts of the dingy court in which they lived, unless it was to wander into some of the wide streets, and look up with wonder and awe at the grand houses they saw there. The sweet green fields, the fresh country lanes, the bright hedge-flowers, which are the delight of many children, were unknown joys to them. Poor Bill sometimes used to stretch out his little thin hand, and cry for the many-coloured blossoms which he saw in the shop windows, and once a little flower-vendor had given him a tiny bunch of lilies of the valley and a sweet-smelling rose, and he had clutched at them greedily, and refused to give them up, even when he went to bed that night.

They had neither father nor mother those two poor children of whom I am writing; their father had died when Bill was quite a baby, and then their mother worked hard to get food for them; and at last there came a day when she said she could not go out as usual, and she lay on her bed for a fortnight or more, and Patty did her best to nurse her, and a neighbour used to come in and help her sometimes, and she fetched a doctor, but he only shook his head and said it was too late. The next morning, just when the summer sun was shedding its first rays of light into the dreary room, the poor woman bade Patty kiss her, and told her to take care of the baby, and when the neighbour came in quite early to see how matters were going on, she found the mother lying there with closed eyes and a smile upon her face, that had never been there when she was alive, and Patty was fast asleep holding Bill tenderly in her little arms.

She had never been taught her duty to GOD, that poor thing who had gone to what we humbly hope was rest from toil ; she had let some friend take Patty to Church to be baptised, because she (the friend) had said it was good for the child ; and for the same reason she herself had taken Bill there after his father died.

She did not know what she was doing, poor soul ; not a thought of the loving care into which she was placing her boy was in her mind ; she had never been taught anything ; she had lived as many and many an one does live in this great city of ours, an almost heathen life ; but she had been a good wife to her husband, and a kind mother to her children ; and GOD is very merciful, and JESUS died to save us.

Sometimes, as I walk along the crowded streets, I marvel whether in the last great Day He will show mercy to those to whom He has given riches, and knowledge, and the power to do good, and who have neglected their opportunities, and allowed souls to perish for want of being taught,—for to whom much is given, of them shall much be required.

And poor Patty of course had grown up in ignorance of all that a Christian child ought to know,—her love for Bill was her religion, she knew no other, poor child, but this affection for her little brother was the one soft spot in the girl's heart; to keep him from want, there was nothing she would not do, no act of self-denial from which she would shrink.

She could never be away from him long; she used to go about the streets selling potatoes and cabbages for a woman who kept a costermonger's shop at the corner of Fleur-de-lis Court, and she used to wheel along a little cart, and put Bill on the top of the potatoes, and watch over him as tenderly as though he had been a little prince.

On that day when my story begins she had done her morning's work, and was hurrying home to give Bill his dinner, when she met a neighbour of hers, a girl by name Harriet Groves, a great rough maiden, who always said she wished she had been a boy, because she was so fond of fighting. As the wish could not be gratified, she was not to be deterred from her

pugilistic propensities, and whenever she could
get a chance of dealing a blow to any one she
did it,—not really from malice, but because it
was evidently a gratification to her to use her
fists.

She had tried to push Patty off the pavement,
and Patty resented the insult, as was but natural
perhaps, then Harriet had given her a slap, and
had afterwards dealt another, a very gentle one
it must be confessed, to Bill.

Whereupon all Patty's anger was aroused, and
she had spoken those wicked words to the girl
which I have already quoted,—" I tell you I
hate you . . . wait till the first time I gets a
chance, and won't I give it you, that's all."

There had been one standing near who had
seen the quarrel, and heard the threat, and
whose heart had sunk within her as she looked
at the young face distorted by passion, and saw
the mingled anger and love struggling within her
for the mastery.

And this one was a Sister of Mercy, a gentle
woman who had left a home of luxury and ease
to give her life to GOD, to spend her days
amongst the poor, and the sick, and the sinful,
because by doing this she knew she was spend-
ing her days with JESUS, that He, the Incarnate

God, was ever near her in the persons of those to whom she ministered.

"My child," and the sweetest voice that Patty had ever heard sounded on her ears; "My child, I am so sorry for your poor little brother."

Sister Ruth must have learned a lesson of skilful diplomacy ere she spoke those words, for none others could have found their way in like manner into the girl's heart.

"Oh, ma'am, he is very bad, but he is such a good little fellow," and all the anger went out of Patty's face then, and only the great deep love shone out of her eyes.

"Yes, I am sure he is good; do you think you could come to the Children's Service to-morrow afternoon in the Church?"

"Please, I don't know what that means, and I haven't any money to get in."

"My child, you don't want money, but you will hear of all God's love for His children, and it will help you to bear things."

"God!"—and Patty looked wonderingly into the sweet face; "Mother talked of God afore she went away, but I didn't know what she meant."

"Will you meet me to-morrow at this corner, and I will take you with me?"

" May I bring Bill ?"

" Yes, of course you may, you couldn't come without him, could you ?"

" No, ma'am, he's only got me in all the world ; mother told me to take care of him."

Sister Ruth was very wise ; she did not do as a great many very good people would have done, scold Ruth about the way she had spoken to Harriet Groves,—she saw how ignorant the poor child was, and so she tried to win her by kind, loving words, and gentle ways, and in the end, as we shall see, she conquered.

Patty went home to think of the sweet kind face, and all thoughts of Harriet Groves went out of her heart as she rocked Bill to sleep, and wondered what she should see and hear next day at the Church.

She kept her promise ; ten minutes before the time she and Bill were at the place of meeting, and Patty was getting very fidgety when the clock struck three, and no Sister Ruth appeared.

" Where's the lady ?" said Bill, " I want her."

And as he spoke the words the gentle Sister appeared, and the boy held out his little arms to her, and Patty resigned him willingly.

"You're the first as I ever gived him to," she said, "he never would go to any one afore, ma'am."

"Don't call me ma'am,—call me Sister."

Patty laughed. "Lor, I can't do that, it's so funny."

But Bill stroked the soft cheek, and said "Sister" in his little lisping voice, and Patty could not hold out any longer then, and she said, "It is funny, but I'll call you that if you wish it."

They had reached the Church by this time, and they went in together, and both Patty and her little brother gazed round them wonderingly, they had never seen anything so beautiful in all their lives before.

Bill soon went to sleep, and Patty listened to the sweet music, and wondered what it all meant, for she caught a word here and there, but of course she understood nothing about it, only she liked to hear it,—it made her feel as she had never felt before, not quite so sad, not quite so lonely.

There were a great many children in the holy building, some tidily dressed, some all in rags and tatters ; and some one dressed in white, Patty did not then know who it was, spoke to them very kindly, and told them that they had a FATHER in Heaven Who loved them very much, an Elder Brother, Whose Name was JESUS, Who had cared for them so much that He died for them.

He said all this in very plain words indeed, so plain that even poor ignorant Patty understood something of their meaning, and wondered whether there was any one who really loved her and Bill, as "this man in white" said, GOD and JESUS loved all children.

Then he spoke to them about Holy Baptism, and he explained to them that when they were baptised they were brought to Church and their name was given them.

Patty listened very attentively to this, for she felt that she was interested in it; she knew that she and Bill had been taken to Church, but she never knew that any good had come of it, until the preacher said so on that Fourteenth Sunday after Trinity. Afterwards he went on to tell them of the special lesson they were to carry away with them for the day, and he read the Epistle and explained it to them.

He told them that GOD said that those who allowed themselves to be angry, and who hated another, (never mind what wrong they might be

smarting under,) should not inherit the Kingdom of GOD; and he said at last,

" My children, those who belong to JESUS—
those who have received the Spirit of GOD in
Holy Baptism, must be meek and gentle, and
good, and long-suffering, for these are the fruits
of the Spirit. You know what it is to bear the
injuries that others do you, without getting angry,
or seeking in any way to harm them. Sometimes I know children are very fond of teasing
each other, and you, none of you, like to be
teased, do you? I am sure I did not when I
was a little boy; well, when one of your companions teases you in any way and you feel inclined to answer rudely, even sometimes to strike
the offender, think of JESUS Who bore more
suffering for you than you can ever bear for Him,
and say a little prayer and ask Him to help you
to be meek and gentle, because if you are not so,
if you do not bear things patiently for His sake,
He will not take you to live with Him in that
bright beautiful land which He came down from
heaven to earth to win for you."

When the service was over Sister Ruth went home
with Patty and Bill—such a home as it was, such
a miserable dark dirty room, looking out upon
the chimney pots of the neighbouring houses.

"I must get Bill's tea," said Patty; "he'll wake up in a few minutes and want it, and I never likes to keep him waiting."

"Do so, my child, and let me see if I can help you."

Patty was highly amused at the idea, and she and Ruth got quite merry over the preparations for the meal, and the latter drew a cake and a little packet of loaf sugar out of her pocket, and said that she had been going to see an old woman in the court and had provided herself with these delicacies for her, but Bill and Patty should have them, she could go to the Home and get some more for Granny Lobbs.

Then, whilst Bill still slept, very gently and kindly the Sister spoke to Patty of the words the Priest had spoken that afternoon.

You all know what she said about the love of GOD and of JESUS; for you, dear children, who read this little tale, have all been taught these things. I will not repeat them here, I will only ask you when you say your prayers to ask our FATHER in heaven to show mercy to all those little ones who have never heard His holy Name. Because of all His goodness to you, will you do this?

When Sister Ruth came to that part about

the Fruits of the Spirit, and about bearing things patiently, Patty looked very uncomfortable.

"There's one girl," she said, "as aggravates me awful; and I've promised to give it her well the first time I gets a chance; mustn't I, Sister?"

"No, my dear, you must try to bear the aggravation, and by so doing you will please GOD."

"I should like to please Him," answered Patty, "but I don't think I can; I must give it to Harriet Groves, indeed I must, because she was so wicked to my little Bill."

Then Patty detailed the circumstances of the quarrel the day before, and Sister Ruth did not let out that she had seen and heard all; she only made the girl kneel by her side, and she said a little prayer and asked GOD to make His child meek and gentle as all Christian children ought to be.

By this time Bill was awake, ready to talk and be quite merry over his cake, and as Sister Ruth saw the sister's loving care for her little brother she felt that the nature that was capable of such unselfish love must be capable too, of better things.

She asked Patty to come to the Home every

evening and to bring Bill with her, and she promised to teach her to read and to tell her more about GOD and about JESUS.

All through those autumn evenings Bill's sister might be seen carrying her little brother to the Home, and the girl had never been seen to look as happy as she did then, a new brightness, and a new joy, had come into the poor desolate life of the little London girl.

She was a sharp intelligent child, and she learned quickly, and remembered well, and Sister Ruth was very proud of her pupil, and very thankful when one evening Patty whispered,

" I seed Harriet Groves to-day for the first time since that night; she've been away in the country; and I runned round a corner to get out of her way, and—and I said a little prayer, please Sister."

" That was right, my child; you see GOD kept you safe from harm, because you thought of Him."

Christmas was very near now, the time when all people, when all Christian children ought more especially to bring forth the Fruits of the Spirit, to be more than usually loving, and meek, and gentle, because of the meek and lowly SAviour Who was born as at this time in the cold manger for our sakes.

Patty had learned a great deal since that September afternoon when we first saw her; and even Bill was beginning to say some little hymns, and answer some little questions, and his sister's pride in his accomplishments was really a touching sight.

They were both looking forward to the great glad Feast, Bill being especially delighted at the prospect of a magic lantern which was to be exhibited, and where he had been told he should see lots of lions and tigers.

One evening as Sister Ruth sat in her own room there came a quick hurried knock at the door, and before she could give permission to enter, Patty sobbing piteously, her hat on one side, her mouth bleeding, stood before her.

"Oh, Sister, Sister, I didn't say the prayer, and Harriet Groves came up and insulted me, and she took a bit of holly out of Bill's hand, and I set him down on a door step, and I runned after her and gived it her well, and she gived it me back, and now what is to become of me? I can never be good no more."

Sister Ruth made the poor child sit down, and

whilst she told her how wrong she had been, she tried to soothe her and to make her see how temptations must come into the lives of all GOD's children, and how we must all fight to the end, and ask JESUS, Who knows our temptations, to raise us up again when we have fallen. And Patty went away somewhat comforted, but still very miserable.

"Oh, Bill, Bill," she murmured, as she bent over the sleeping boy that night, "it's hard to bear things when she touches you; but I know I'm very wicked, and I did want to be good."

Christmas came, and Bill was very happy at the sight of the magic lantern, and Patty was glad because he was glad, but what she liked were the services in the Church; the beautiful hymns, the bright flowers—all telling of the great joy that had come to sinful man.

She used to see Harriet Groves sometimes, but she generally contrived to get out of her way; and once when she came across her, and the rude girl began her foolish teasing ways, and took Bill's cap off his head and ran away with it, Patty said her little prayer, and then she laughed, and picked the cap out of the gutter quite good-temperedly.

Another day the snow lay thick upon the ground, and there was a sharp frost, which made walking very dangerous, and Patty had some difficulty in getting her cart along, whilst Bill sat triumphantly amongst the potatoes and cabbages, intensely delighted with watching the boys sliding and snowballing each other. As Patty stopped at the house of one of her customers, and was measuring out the potatoes, she heard a sharp cry, a wail of pain; she knew that cry but too well, Bill was in pain, Bill was hurt in some way; she flew up the area steps and there she saw Harriet Groves standing by the side of the cart trying to lift the boy out.

"Be quiet, Harriet," she cried, "don't hurt him."

Harriet turned sharply round, and rushed to the gate, which she pulled to, with all her might; Patty tried to open it, but the other was the stronger of the two, the poor child's foot slipped, and the next minute she was lying at the foot of the steps pale and senseless, whilst Bill screaming lustily, kept his seat in the cart. A crowd very soon assembled.

"It's she as did it," said a butcher boy, pointing to Harriet, "I saw her, she was teasing of the little chap, and she wouldn't let the girl get to him, she shut the gate, and when Patty tried to open it she slipped back and fell."

"You'll be took up for murder," said a shoe-black, who was standing by, and Harriet thinking discretion the better part of valour, ran off as fast as she could.

"What is to be done with her?" asked a policeman, lifting poor Patty gently in his strong arms, "where's her home?"

"Take her to the Sisters," said the shoeblack, "they are sure to be good to her."

"I believe you're right, my man, that's the best place for her."

"Take me too, take me too," cried poor neglected Bill; whereupon the shoeblack took him up and carried him off behind the policeman to the Home.

Sister Ruth happened to be just coming out of the door when she met the strange little procession. She was soon told what had happened, and Bill's sister, and Bill himself, were carried up into the Infirmary and laid upon the cleanest bed upon which they had ever lain in all their lives. After a time Patty opened her eyes and looked about her.

"I ain't angry, Harriet, I ain't indeed, I wasn't

going to strike you, I said the prayer; I only wanted you not to hurt my little Bill."

Sister Ruth saw that her mind was wandering.

"My child, do you not know me?"

"Yes, Sister, yes; please don't be angry, I was not going to strike her, indeed I wasn't." And then Patty closed her eyes again, and did not open them for many hours.

The doctor said that her hip was fractured, and it would be a long long time before she was well; her head too had received some injury, which was not likely to be easily got over.

Very tenderly, for JESUS' sake, the Sisters nursed the poor child, and she was very good and patient, and always so thankful for what was done for her.

They often brought Bill in to see her; they would not let him be in the Infirmary altogether, but he was very happy, and getting quite fat and strong, and Patty, although she was never quite content when he was out of her sight, submitted to all that was required of her.

One day when Sister Ruth was sitting by the side of Patty's bed, she was told that a girl wanted to see her. "She will not give her name, Sister, but she's brought something for Patty."

"For me! there's no one outside as cares for me."

Sister Ruth went to see who it could be. A great tall girl stood in the hall holding a small paper parcel in her hand.

"If you please, how is Patty?"

"She is very ill."

"Will she die?"

"My child, GOD only knows; the doctor said this morning he was afraid she would."

The girl's head was bent upon her hands, and Sister Ruth fancied she heard a sob.

"Will you give her this crab? I've buyed it for her; she once told me she was very partial to them."

"Thank you, my child; will you tell me your name? I fancy I have seen you somewhere before."

"My name is Harriet Groves, and it's my fault that she's dying."

And before Sister Ruth could answer Harriet had made her way out of the door, which had just been opened to admit some one else, and was running wildly down the street. Sister Ruth went back to Patty and told her who her visitor had been. Not one tear had the child shed through all her pain and suffering; but now the big drops rolled down her pale cheeks as she listened to all the story of Harriet's grief.

"Sister, might I see her? will you fetch her?"

"Yes, my child, if you wish it."

That evening Harriet Groves stood looking at the girl who through her fault was lying there.

"Patty, I'm sorry; I'll never tease you nor Bill no more."

"No, I know you won't; don't cry, Harriet, I ain't angry, indeed I ain't; if I was, I couldn't hope to go, where I hopes I'm going soòn. Sister Ruth will tell you about the Fruits of the Spirit. Kiss me, Harriet, and come and see Bill sometimes."

And Harriet kissed her and went away.

Ere another day had passed Patty had gone from her little Bill. They had brought him to her at the last, and she had smiled, and said,

"His little legs is getting quite fat; Sister Ruth says he'll be able to walk soon, and you see then he'll not want me as he have done. You'll teach him to be long-suffering and gentle, and you'll teach Harriet too."

These were the last words that Bill's sister

ever spoke. And now Sister Ruth is trying to fulfil her last prayer, and in Bill's gentle ways and Harriet's very gradual improvement she thinks the prayer is answered.

It is a hard lesson that we all of us have to learn—that lesson of perfect forgiveness which this Fourteenth Sunday after Trinity teaches us. We are all so ready to resent an injury, so anxious to stand up for ourselves and fight our own battles, so prone to render railing for railing instead of the blessings which we have been told by the LORD of all meekness and gentleness ought to be bestowed upon our enemies, even upon those who hate us and use us spitefully.

For what suffering can be like the suffering of JESUS? what woe like His woe? Think of the Crown of Thorns that was placed in very mockery upon His brow; think of the Blood that poured down His Sacred Face for our sakes; think of the cruel stripes that fell upon His shoulders—those shoulders that were to bear the weight of the painful cross, and when we have thought of all this, when we have asked the HOLY SPIRIT to help us to follow our most perfect Pattern, then, by GOD's help, we shall be able to bring forth those fruits of love, joy, peace, long-suffering, gentleness, goodness, faith, meekness, and temperance, which shall make us meet for our Master's Kingdom.

THE LESSON THAT THE LILIES TAUGHT.

ﬁfteenth Sunday after Trinity.

'Sweet nurslings of the vernal skies,
  Bathed in soft airs and fed with dew,
What more than magic in you lies,
  To fill the heart's fond view?
In childhood's sports, companions gay,
In sorrow, on life's downward way,
How soothing!   In our last decay
  Memorials prompt and true."

"OH dear, oh dear, what shall we do if it
    rains to-morrow ?"

I was a little girl of some ten or eleven years
old, and I was looking ruefully out of the dining-
room window one Sunday afternoon in September, watching the rain as it dripped, and
dripped, and dripped, as though it never meant
to stop dripping again.   And the next day we

were to go out, my brothers and I, to spend a long day in the country with some young cousins of ours, and everything depended upon the weather, and Harold had been tapping, or rather hammering at the barometer, and had just put in his head with the unwelcome intelligence that it was going back as fast as anything,—then he had returned to his hammering, as though some atmospheric change might have occurred during that minute, but as I heard the repeated taps my heart sank within me, for I knew that Harold had no better news to tell, and again I sighed and repeated the words, " Oh dear, oh dear, what shall we do if it rains to-morrow ?"

Many a long year has elapsed since that dismal Sunday afternoon, GOD has sent many a joy and many a sorrow into my life since then, but my memory takes me back with strange distinctness to the dear old dining-room, with the pictures of our ancestors hanging upon the oak walls, and the fire, the first by the way that we had had that year, burning brightly in the large, old-fashioned grate.

" My little Nettie, what is the matter ? why are you so doleful ?"

" Oh, Aunt Agnes, isn't the rain a bore ? do you think it will be fine to-morrow ?"

"I don't know, Nettie darling, I hope for your sakes it may; but if it is not—"

"Oh, please don't say that there is a single chance of its not being fine," I interrupted eagerly, "indeed I couldn't bear it."

I remember that Aunt Agnes' sweet face had something of a grave look upon it, as she smiled and took me upon her knee and said,

"My darling, it would be such a little thing to bear, such a little disappointment, although I am quite willing to own that it *would* be a disappointment; and, Nettie, there are such great troubles that come into the lives of some people, and the little things look so very small, and so very insignificant when we contrast them with the great ones."

I thought that Aunt Agnes' voice faltered a little as she spoke, and as I looked into the dear old face, upon which lines of care had left their mark, I remember I stooped and kissed it, and stroked the silvery hair with loving hand, —next to my father and mother and brothers, I loved Aunt Agnes better than any one else in the world.

"Mother sent me down, Nettie, to ask you if you could say your Collect, she has sent the boys off to Church, but she thinks it is too wet for you to go, and she has a headache and is lying down, so she has asked me to take her place this afternoon."

"Oh, Aunt Agnes, I am so glad."

"Glad, Nettie, that the dear mother has a headache?"

"No, not that, but glad that you have come down to me, for you will tell me a story, will you not, dear Auntie? and your stories are always new, and mother's are getting just a little wee bit old, she has to tell them over so often." ·

I said my Collect, that for the Fifteenth Sunday after Trinity, and Aunt Agnes explained to me what was meant by man's frailty, even the weakness of our mortal nature, which only by GOD's help can be kept from hurtful things, and then in her sweet low voice she read the words of the Gospel for the day, and when she had got to the end of it, she repeated some of the verses, as though she wished to impress them upon my memory. "Consider the lilies of the field, how they grow; they toil not, neither do they spin, and yet I say unto you that even Solomon in all his glory was not arrayed like one of these. Wherefore if GOD so clothe the grass of the field, which to-day is, and to-morrow is cast into the oven, shall He not much more clothe you, O ye of little faith ? Seek ye first the kingdom of GOD and His righteousness, and all these things shall be added unto you. Take therefore no thought for the morrow, for the morrow shall take thought for the things of itself : sufficient unto the day is the evil thereof."

"Nettie darling," said Aunt Agnes, "I am going to tell a story, but you must let me say just a few words to you first about this Holy Gospel, which you know is part of our Blessed LORD's Sermon on the Mount.

"He wanted to teach the people a lesson of faith and trust in GOD, and He wants to teach us this lesson every day of our lives.

"When He says that we are to take no thought for our lives, for what we shall eat or what we shall drink, and what we shall put on, He does not mean that we are not to labour honestly for our living. He Himself worked in S. Joseph's shop at Nazareth, sanctifying all work and all labour for evermore. He only means that such things must not have the first place in our thoughts, that we must think of Him, and of His honour and glory first ; that all we do must be done for Him, and then He will give us all else that we want. We must not worry ourselves with thoughts for the morrow, for the morrow shall take thought for the things of itself : sufficient unto the day is the evil thereof.

"Sometimes, Nettie dear, if we would think of this, it would make us less inclined to grumble and to fidget about things over which we can have no possible control,—the weather, for instance," and Aunt Agnes' funny smile lurked about the corners of her mouth.

"Then mustn't I think about the weather tomorrow, as to whether it will rain or be fine ?" I asked somewhat anxiously.

"I will not say that, dear, it would hardly be in human nature,—certainly not in the human nature of ten years old,—not to hope that the clouds will all have cleared away, and that it will be a bright sunshiny day ; but, Nettie, I want you to learn not to fret about little things, not to worry over what may never come to pass. I have seen you do it more than once since I have been here,—the other evening you thought that Maggie Collinson would not be able to have you there to tea, because her mamma was ill, and you were cross and discontented the whole morning, and after all you were able to go ; dear child, these seem little things, but it is the way

in which we meet the small crosses and vexa-
tions that come into our lives, that help us to
bear the greater troubles that GOD in His mercy,
and His love, sees fit to send us.

"There are not two ways of dealing with
them. The same hand sends us the little worries,
and the heavy sorrows; and to Him we must
take them both, lay them both at the foot of
the cross, and ask Him to bless them to our
soul's health. All will be easy to bear if we
trust in Him; if we are thankful for the present
and leave the future to Him Who feeds the
fowls of the air, and clothes the sweet lilies of
the field."

"Then I'll be glad if it is fine to-morrow, but
I won't be cross if it should rain, Aunt Agnes,"
I said.

"Yes, my darling, that is the right way to
take things, for GOD sends us days of sunshine
and days of rain, as He sees best, and so we
must be thankful for both, and praise Him for
all His infinite goodness. And now, Nettie,
I'll tell you a story of a little maiden who gave
up all her ways to GOD and never thought of
herself."

It was a wild bleak barren coast upon which

the little fishing village of Addlestone was situated, there was nothing to be seen but the beach, and the wide expanse of sea, and the huge rocks in the distance, and quite at the far end of the bay was the chapel which the Lord of the Manor had caused to be built in memory of one of his brave young sons who had been drowned in the pitiless ocean and who lay beneath the great deep, waiting until that day when the sea shall give up her dead.

In Addlestone itself there were but three or four fishers' huts, it was from some of the neighbouring villages that the sailors and their wives and children came to the chapel, and every Sunday and sometimes on week-days, worshipped GOD in faith, and sacrament and prayer.

It was on a Sunday morning in September, a great many years ago, that a mother and a little girl left one of the Addlestone huts, and took their way to the fisherman's chapel.

The poor woman looked pale and ill, and sorrowful, and she leant upon the little one's shoulder for support, and ever and anon she gazed tearfully back to the home she had just left.

And Elsie (that was the child's name) looked back also, and then she said,

" I don't think father will come to-day, mother, do you think he will ?"

There was no answer but a deep-drawn sigh, Mary Farmer's heart was too full for words that morning, and Elsie looked up lovingly into the pale face, and as she did so a strange fear came upon the child's heart.

She had heard the neighbours say that her mother was not long for this world; and she had hardly taken in the words, hardly been able to realise, poor little maid, all the greatness of that trouble that was coming upon her.

And, Nettie, (said Aunt Agnes, drawing me more closely to her side,) it is a part of GOD'S infinite mercy that we cannot foresee what will happen on the morrow, cannot fathom what the full extent of that anguish will be, that GOD may think fit to send us in very love. There was only *One* Who knew beforehand what depths of woe He should have to pass through, Who felt beforehand the keen suffering that was coming upon Him,—and this *One* was our Blessed LORD ; and it was a part of His agony—ay, the worst part that so it should be,—that the GOD-like nature saw what the Man must endure, and so the Incarnate shrank from the contemplation of the cup His FATHER had given Him to drink, and shed great drops of His own most Precious Blood ere He bowed His meek Head and said, "Not My will, but Thine be done."

But, my child, I must not tire you with these thoughts that come into my old head, but must go on with my story.

Elsie did not speak again; she only tried to walk quietly, to suit her quick bounding footsteps to those poor lagging ones of her mother's, and another ten minutes brought them to the little chapel, and Elsie saw that as her mother knelt there the weary, anxious, troubled look went from her face.

The preacher's text that day was from the words of the Gospel for the Fifteenth Sunday after Trinity, (I have forgotten to tell you, Nettle, that it was this Sunday about which I am writing,) "Take no thought for the morrow, for the morrow shall take thought for the things of itself: sufficient unto the day is the evil thereof."

I am not going to tell you the words he spoke, I have told you the sense of them already, when I was trying to explain the Gospel to you just now, and you would only be weary if I said them over again; I need only speak of the impression they left upon the hearts of Elsie and her mother.

" You are better now," said the child, as they walked home again along the beach, whilst the ever advancing and receding waves came playing at their feet.

" Yes, my dear, I'm better, I've learned more faith and trust since I went in there,—I'll try and bear whatever GOD sends me, and leave the morrow in His hands ; and you'll do the same, won't you, darling ?"

" Yes," and the blue eyes were raised to the pale face, with an expression of childlike trust, "yes, mother, I'll be a good girl, and try to bear things, when GOD sends them to me ;" and again there came upon the poor little heart that faint foreshadowing of fear which she could hardly understand, only she knew that it had to do with mother and with her going away.

A man was standing at the door of the hut as the mother and child drew near.

A good looking fellow enough was that Ralph Farmer, but there was a scowl upon his brow, and a fierce light in his grey eye that caused Mary's cheek to grow even a shade paler than usual, and that made Elsie clutch at her mother's dress, and try to hide.

" Come on, both of you, I've been waiting for my dinner this half-hour."

"I'm sorry, Ralph dear," was the meek and gentle answer; "I wish you had not waited for us; I cannot walk as fast as I used to do, you see, and that makes me late."

"Well, come along now," he repeated more kindly, and as he looked upon the weak bending form there was a shade of softness upon the hard face, that was not often to be seen there.

The three sat down in silence to their meal, —the last to which they would sit down together for a very long time—ay, would it ever be so again? would they ever in the days that were to come look upon each other's faces as they did now in the little hut by the sea?

Elsie was the first to speak.

"What time are you going, father?"

"At three o'clock, child, and it will take me two hours or more to walk into Brightsea."

"And when will you come back?"

He turned away, and looked out of the window far away, to where the crested waves broke against the huge rocks, and then he said in a hoarse voice,

"I dare say in a year you will have me back again."

He looked out upon those waves for a long time, he could not bear to see his wife's face;

he could imagine the expression of agony that was on it then.

For Mary loved her husband truly, and it was hard to think that he was going away from her for all those long months. And in his way he cared for her—only he cared most for himself; he was essentially selfish, and if anything put him out that scowl would come upon his brow, and that light in his eye, which his wife and child dreaded to see.

He was not a religious man; he would not often go to Church, and when that morning his wife had begged him to think of how long it might be before they worshipped GOD again in His own most Holy House, and entreated him for this last time to come with her and Elsie, he had pushed her off roughly, and told her that he had other things to do on that morning.

Trade had been very bad in Addlestone for a great many months, and Ralph Farmer had made up his mind to go to sea.

He had got a situation as mate on board a vessel now lying in Brightsea harbour, which was bound for the Chinese seas, and he had received orders to be on board by three o'clock on that Sunday afternoon. Quickly the minutes passed away, and Ralph Farmer called his little girl to him, and said with a strange tenderness in his voice,

"Elsie, you will take care of your mother when I am gone?"

Poor Elsie smiled a little faint smile, and answered,

"I am so small, father, so very very small, but I will do my best, and GOD will take care of her; for He feeds the fowls, and makes the lilies to grow, and He will be good to her and to me. Mr. Hartley said so this morning, and JESUS" (and here the child bowed her head reverently) "said so before He went away to heaven."

Ralph did not answer; whatever good there was in him was stirred up then as he looked at his wife's face, and wondered that he had not noticed before how thin and pale it had got during those last few months.

He got up and clasped her in his arms.

"Good-bye, my girl, take care of yourself; I will write as often as I can, and a year will soon pass away;" and then he stooped and kissed Elsie. "Take care of her, little one," he said, "and of yourself too."

And Elsie answered, "GOD will take care of us, because He cares for the lilies that grow in the field."

He could not wait any longer : he went away as fast as he could, and his wife and child stood at the door, and watched his strong athletic figure out of sight. And he turned and waved his sailor's hat in the air, and that was the last they saw of him, as he rounded the corner of the hill, and so was hidden from their view.

They went back and prayed for him; at least Mary prayed, and Elsie joined her hands, ·and said Amen. And then she threw her arms round her mother's neck, and said, " He told me to take care of you, and I will try to, mammy, —I will ask GOD to teach me how."

They lived their quiet life in the dreary hut, and winter came and went, and once more it was bright spring-time ; and the neighbours said that ere the summer had passed, Mary Farmer would have gone to her rest.

Elsie was a very tender little nurse. She did everything for her mother, and tried to save her trouble in every way ; and she used to listen when she heard others say how ill Mary Farmer was, and then she used to steal away to the beach and cry, all by herself, and ask GOD to take care of mother, and of her, and of father, who was tossing about on the wide sea.

It was a bright June evening, and the door of

the hut was open, and the sea was dancing and sparkling beneath the flickering rays of the setting sun, and the sailor's wife lay upon her bed, and looked upon all the loveliness of the outer world, and her face was very calm, and there was a sweet smile playing round her lips. She was thinking, it may have been, of a Home more beautiful than any home on earth could ever be,—of a sun that would never set,—of a light that would never wane.

The Priest of the little Chapel had been there that morning, and Mary had made her last confession, and received her last Communion, and now no earthly wish seemed to come between her and those things which belonged to her peace.

Little Elsie ran into the hut, carrying in her hand a beautiful bunch of lilies.

" Mammy, dear mammy, they are for you ; the lilies that GOD has made to grow."

" My darling, thank you ; come to me, Elsie, and listen whilst I speak to you."

And Elsie knelt by the side of the bed, and listened to her mother's words.

" My child, I am going away—going to leave you in GOD's keeping. You must stay here, dear, until father comes home ; it would not do for him to have no welcome back to his home. Once, Elsie, when he went away, just after we were married, I expected him back in the winter, and I used to put a candle in the window every night, to let him see through the darkness that I was waiting for him. Will you do this, Elsie, when the autumn days come?"

"Oh, mammy, mammy, I can't bide here alone."

And the mother took up the sweet white lilies from the bed, and said,

"Elsie, my darling, don't you know the lesson they teach you?"

The child's head was bent low. The poor little frame was trembling all over, for somehow Elsie felt in that moment how dreary her life would be when her mammy had left her; but the sweet unselfish nature triumphed even then, and there was a smile upon the fair face as she raised it, and looked into her mother's.

"They tell us of GOD's care; mother, I will wait for father,—I will not be frightened when I think of the lilies."

"And you will tell him that my last prayer was for him; for him, and for you?"

"Yes, I will tell him."

The sun and the sea were bathed now in one

flood of rosy light, and the dying woman's eyes were fixed upon the distant horizon, as though she would fain gaze athwart that fair beauty of the summer's night, and see what lay beyond. And then again she looked at the lilies.

" My darling, GOD made them, so white and so pure."

She closed her eyes then; those sweet flowers were the last things of earth which she saw as Elsie held them up before her, and said,

" Yes, and He will make me pure, if I pray to Him."

The thin hands were joined in prayer, and when the old woman who lived next door came in to see how Mary Farmer was, she told Elsie that her mother had gone to the Angels.

The little maiden did not cry; she placed the lilies upon the still breast, and then she knelt down and said her evening prayers, and wondered whether her mother heard her simple words.

Doubt it not, Elsie, for did she not always hear your voice on earth? and is not her love for you keener, purer, better in that land where she has gone to pray for father and for you ?

They buried the sailor's wife in the little churchyard by the sea, where the waves dashed ceaselessly against the old time-worn wall, seeming to sing a low soft requiem for those who have gone to their rest. And Elsie planted some lilies on her grave; and when the summer waned, she picked the last one that was likely to bloom that year, and laid it in her mother's Prayer-book, to give to father when he should come home.

She lived alone in that dreary hut,—that little maiden over whose head scarcely ten summers had passed,—and when autumn came, and when at night the wind howled fiercely and the sea roared, as the huge waves broke in upon the shore, she would lie upon her bed and think of her father, and pray Him Who cared for the lilies to bring the sailor safe home.

A letter had come from him just after her mother died, and she had taken it to old Martha Hubbard next door, and she had not been able to decipher it; so then she walked over to the clergyman's house, which was a long way off, and she got him to read it to her, and he told her how her father said that he hoped to be home in November.

"I will ask in Church that he may come home safely, my little maid."

"Thank you, sir, I am sure he will, because

ever since he went away I have asked GOD Who takes care of the lilies to take care of him."

And the Priest looked at the child, and there came into his mind the words of JESUS when He spoke of little children, "Of such is the kingdom of heaven."

From that day Elsie never went to bed without putting the light in the window, as her mother had told her to do. And she waited and watched and prayed until her father should come home.

One dreary November day, when the sky was dark and lowering, and the wind moaned fiercely through the leafless trees, and the sea dashed furiously against the rocks, a fisherman came home from Brightsea, and said that the "Mary Jane" (Ralph Farmer's vessel) was in sight, and Elsie knew that her father must be home now before long; and still she said her prayers, and that night she put two lights in the upper window of the little hut.

When evening came, the gale became a hurricane, more terrible than any of the Addlestone people ever remembered to have witnessed.

Elsie went to bed. "Father will be home in the morning," she said to herself; "Ben Robin-

son said the 'Mary Jane' must have got in
before the storm got to its worst."

As the little maiden slept the sound sleep of
childhood the terrible hurricane rose to its
height; the sea broke fiercely through the wall
which had been built to protect the Addlestone
people from the inroads of those pitiless waves.

Every one was astir; the water had got into
the huts; men and women and children were
struggling for dear life.

Then a cry arose,—" The little one—Elsie—is
all alone."

There were no lights in the window now : all
was darkness; and a man made his way through
the fast gathering waters into the room where
the child slept.

She was awake now; the chill of the rushing
waters had roused her from that sound dream-
less slumber.

" Elsie, Elsie," said Ralph Farmer's voice in
agony.

But Elsie did not hear. "O GOD, Who
takest care of the lilies, take care of me, and
bring father home safe through the storm ; and
oh, take me through the cold waters to—"

She did not speak again, those cold waters
were rising above her head now; and the next

minute a pair of strong arms were round her, and Elsie's head was on her father's shoulder, and she was murmuring something about the lilies.

Next morning not a trace of the fishermen's huts was to be found—all had been swept away during that night of terror,—but not a life had been lost; and at the thanksgiving service in the little chapel Elsie knelt by her father's side, bright and happy. He took her to Brightsea for a while, and he told her that he should never let her go to Church alone any more,—that he would go with her always.

He did not go to sea again. Some neat cottages rose in the place of the old tumble-down huts, and there is not a happier home in Addlestone than that of Ralph Farmer.

The father and daughter talked often in hushed whispers of the gentle wife and mother who had gone to the better land, and Elsie's father often said,

"For her sake, little one, I will be good to you : I will try and make your life happy."

"Oh, father, GOD is very good to me, and I am so thankful."

"And you have no fears for the future, Elsie ?"

"Oh no, for GOD Who takes care of the lilies, says that if we think of Him first all else will be right, and that sufficient unto the day is the evil thereof."

Aunt Agnes' story was ended, and I think I had learned the lesson of the lilies. For the satisfaction of my younger readers the September day that followed that Fifteenth Sunday after Trinity was as bright and glorious a day as could be, and the boys and I enjoyed ourselves thoroughly.

"Gentle JESUS, meek and mild,
 Take, O take me for Thy child;
 All my life, O let it be,
 My best joy to think of Thee.
     Gentle JESUS, meek and mild,
     Take, O take me for Thy child.

"When my eyes are closed in sleep,
 Through the night my slumbers keep;
 Make my latest thought to be
 How to give my heart to Thee.
     Gentle JESUS, meek and mild,
     Take, O take me for Thy child.

"Teach me, when the sunbeam bright
 Calls me with its golden light,

How my waking thoughts may be
Turned, dear SAVIOUR, unto Thee.
　Gentle JESUS, meek and mild,
　Take, O take me for Thy child.

"Thus, sweet SAVIOUR, day and night
Thou shalt guide my steps aright,
And my dying words shall be,
LORD, I give my soul to Thee.
　Gentle JESUS, meek and mild,
　Take, O take me for Thy child."

Milton Keynes UK
Ingram Content Group UK Ltd.
UKHW040139160224
437928UK00003B/33